KING STREET
TO
KING'S ROAD

A Journey Through Social
And Medical History

D0294367

Jacqueline Heron Wray

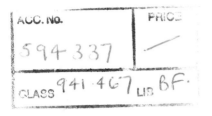

While all the stories in this book are true, some names and identifying details have been changed to protect the privacy of the people involved.

DEDICATION

For Gran and Papa, I miss you and think of you every day; and for my amazing dad, you are truly one in a million.

CONTENTS

ACKNOWLEDGMENTS

Love and thanks to Mike, Jemma and Lisa who have always believed in me and encouraged me to chase my dreams.

Gratitude to Alex Bartley and Jean Murphy for their patience, reading and editing skills.

Thanks to Frank Beattie who took time out of his busy life to offer advice and encouragement to a newbie. Also, thanks to Pat McDonald for jogging my memory about Kilmarnock Infirmary Consultants and nursing staff.

Sincere thanks to James McCallum Manderson (Callum) for sharing his amazing stories and escapades.

And last but not least, thanks to my amazing dad for always being there for me. Love you, Dad.

Figure 1: *Nil desperandum*

PREFACE

I stood at the bus stop on Chelsea Bridge Road and looked across at The Lister Hospital.

What the hell have I done? I asked myself.

A prestigious job in SW1W. Excellent salary. I was Outpatient Manager in charge of three floors of outpatient clinics, a laser department, plus I oversaw Chelsea Consulting Rooms, a private GP practice, in Lower Sloane Street. So many opportunities, so many amazing colleagues, so many famous faces, and here I was walking away from it all. But the deed had been done, my resignation letter was probably winging its way to our HR department as I stood waiting for the number 44 bus. My boss, Jo, had expressed her disappointment, but thankfully she was supportive and understood my reasons.

My thoughts wandered back to 1969. That year I had been a patient in Seafield sick children's hospital in Ayr. I was the oldest in the ward and I had had my tonsils and adenoids removed. It had not been a routine procedure in that I haemorrhaged to such an extent that I was taken back to theatre where presumably the bleeding was stopped by cautery or whatever method was in use then, and I was given a blood transfusion. This resulted in me being a patient there for about a week instead of a couple of days. Long enough to take in every movement made by the nurses, the crisp uniforms with starched white aprons and perky caps on top of their heads. Even at the age of nine I could sense the camaraderie and light-hearted humour which seeped and flowed between the nurses like blood from haemorrhaging tonsils.

Much to my family's surprise, primarily because I had hated my time in hospital so much and cried every night begging to leave, the first thing I asked for when I got home was a dress-up nurse's outfit, I remember it now. A blue and white stripy dress with a little white apron attached. The apron had a red cross on the bib and a rather garish image of a fob watch stamped on it. The simple cap, no more than a strip of white cloth with another red cross on it, was held in place on my head by a thin piece of elastic. When I say held on my head, I mean that it slipped up and off at every opportunity. I felt sad about my lack of hair. My mum insisted that it should be kept short and I dreamed of having long hair just like Alexandra Bastedo in 'The Champions'. I just knew that if I had a beautiful hair bun on top of my head that the nurse's cap would have stayed firmly in place; it was quite frankly a huge disappointment (I tried to make my own using one of my dad's handkerchiefs with varying levels of success). The outfit was topped off with a shoulder-length blue cape piped with red ribbon which tied at the neck and frayed after the first use. I thought I was the bee's knees when I wore it and insisted that every doll and teddy bear I owned should also have his or her Ts and As removed.

Little did I know that in less than ten years' time I would be wearing a nurse's uniform for real, and that the cap although disappointingly made of thick card, would stay firmly in place around my up-do.

The decision to become a nurse took me to several interesting places to practice and now the last place of employment was to be The Lister.

The following is my journey which has taken me from a small village on the west coast of Scotland to the north of Scotland, East Lothian, America, The Cotswolds, and Hertfordshire. I am not extraordinary by any stretch of the imagination, but I feel the need to share my story if only for Holly and Billy (my niece and nephew), and perhaps one day if I am blessed with grandchildren.

Like most journeys, there was much to discover, and plenty which passed me by. I have discovered that my eyes were often oblivious to what was right in front of them, in more ways than one.

I have always been fascinated by old buildings and social history and have come to appreciate that places I have lived and worked had more than their fair share of both.

Regrettably, I remained unaware of the plethora of history on my own doorstep when I was growing up in Ayrshire. However, when I began to research my family tree in 2014, I uncovered more about my past than I could ever have imagined, from Dad being interviewed on The One O'Clock Gang, a popular television programme in the 1960s, to Cousin Callum's escapades in Moscow at the height of the Cold War.

A large part of my journey has been spent in hospitals and in doctors' surgeries working as a nurse and midwife. As I write this, my family are pulling together as families do, to help Mum and Dad. Mum has Alzheimer's. This cruel and progressive condition affects everyone it meets and is totally ruthless. Mum becoming one of the ever-increasing number of victims, has made me realise how precious memories are, and how easy it is to forget details which we may not think are important. I decided to write mine down while I can still remember them, and while I have relatives alive who can fill in some of the gaps.

I have spent many hours, days, weeks, and months using the Ancestry UK website. I discovered that I may be the 22nd great-granddaughter of Robert the Bruce, and wept about the tragic life of Marjorie Bruce, but more importantly I have compiled a collection of stories and photographs for future generations of my family. I am certain at least one of them will be interested in where they came from. Relatives have come forward with stories, anecdotes and photographs for which I am most grateful. I am indebted to my father, James Heron, my Aunt Margaret and Uncle Robert McMillan, William Heron, James MacCallum Manderson – my second cousin, and my Auntie Betty Hodge. They put out feelers, asking for information and photographs as well as patiently answering my numerous questions.

My nursing career, which began in Kilmarnock in 1978, with me shopping on King Street, ended when I retired from The Lister Hospital in Chelsea in 2014, where most of my shopping was done on the King's Road. Two very different places, both indelibly etched into my heart.

As I said, I am in no way exceptional or remarkable, but I believe everyone has a story to tell. This is mine and no one else on earth can tell it the way I can, and that alone makes it exclusive and unique.

I could.

But you made me feel that I couldn't.

I should.

But you made me feel like I shouldn't.

I would.

But you told me that I wouldn't

I did.

– J Heron

CHAPTER 1

EARLY DAYS AND EARLY MEMORIES

"No man has a good enough memory to be a successful liar."

- Abraham Lincoln

I was born in Kilmarnock, on the 3rd of December 1959, the first of three children born to Jim and Alice Heron. Brother number one – James Alexander – arrived six years later, on the 12th of November. Alastair made an appearance on the 17th of June 1969 whilst I was on a school trip to Culzean Castle. I remember feeling disappointed when I was told I had another brother; I had been hoping for a sister, but he has turned out okay!

Alastair should be grateful for this choice of name; I seem to remember Mum mentioning, more than once, that Christopher-Robin was a lovely name. I too had quite a narrow escape, apparently, she wanted to call me Chantal, of course, there is nothing wrong with either of these names, but I suspect that they were rather too ornamental for a west coast of Scotland village in the 1960s. Mum eventually came up with the name Jacqueline, the feminine form of the French Jacques, and a variant of James. She loved all things French, and still does.

Jim, as he is more commonly known, was named after his paternal and maternal grandfathers respectively, which was the usual thing to do in those days.

Figure 2: *Me showing signs of attitude!*

When I was born, Kilmarnock was a bustling town with many booming industries including Blackwood and Morton Carpets Kilmarnock (BMK). Granny Lochlon, my maternal grandmother, was a carpet weaver there before she married my grandpa, Alexander Brownlee Lochlon, in 1931. The carpet factory BMK, founded in 1908, was one of the main sources of employment in Kilmarnock for many years. Blackwood Morton & Sons was a company comprised of two Kilmarnock families. As early as the 1750s The Blackwoods were spinners and by 1819, Robert Blackwood was a woollen manufacturer. The Kilmarnock and Riccarton Post Office Directory for 1846-47 listed him as a wool-spinner and manufacturer.

In 1860, James and Robert Blackwood joined to form Blackwood Brothers, but they split in 1882 and formed companies of their own. James took his son Henry D. Blackwood into business with him and Robert Blackwood Junior did likewise with his sons William Ford and James Blackwood. By 1908, William Ford Blackwood was sole partner and he joined forces with Gavin (Guy) Morton to form Blackwood Morton & Sons.

The Morton family had been involved with carpet manufacturing for generations. Alexander Morton was born in Darvel, Ayrshire, in 1844. He bought his first loom at the age of fifteen, and by 1874 he had bought his first curtain factory, also in Darvel.

In 1895, Alexander's son became a partner in the business and by 1898, they had bought another factory in Killybegs, in Ireland, to produce hearth rugs. Gavin (Guy), Alexander's nephew, joined the company as a designer in the 1890s.

In 1906, they introduced 'Sundour Fabrics', specifically created and designed not to fade.

William Ford Blackwood was commissioned to weave for Alexander Morton & Co. in 1908, and during The Great War, Blackwood Morton & Sons produced blankets to aid the war effort.

By 1918, they were manufacturing Chenille Axminster carpets and reversible wool rugs. They went on to purchase Cooke, Sons & Co. of Liversedge, in Yorkshire, in 1938.

When the Second World War started there was little or no demand for carpets and so the BMK factory began making shells for the armed forces. After the war, there was a surge in demand for carpets, but eventually cheap imports led to an end to carpet making in Kilmarnock.

In 2005, the Kilmarnock factory which had housed Scotland's oldest carpet manufacturing company (which was by now owned by Stoddarts) closed its doors for good. A sad end for BMK whose carpets were renowned for their design and quality and were recognised throughout the world. Interestingly, in James Cameron's film 'Titanic' made in 1997, 'D' Deck and the Grand Staircase were fitted with carpets made by Stoddard Carpets, the successor to BMK.

There was also the Saxone shoe making factory, and Glenfield and Kennedy which was a firm of hydraulic engineers where my Grandpa Lochlon worked for a while.

In its heyday, 'The Glen' as it was affectionately known, provided thousands of jobs for the people of Kilmarnock. During the Second World War, they made floodgates for the London Underground, allowing some of the deeper tube stations to be used as air-raid shelters. Glenfield and Kennedy also invented, built and donated the only wave-making machine in the UK at that time (and for three decades) to Kilmarnock Swimming Baths. During the Second World War, armed forces from Britain, Canada and America used the pool with its simulated ocean waves for training purposes.

Rowallan Creamery was established in 1886 by John Wallace as a 'butterine' or margarine factory. The creamery produced Banquet margarine, which was very popular at that time, and several other dairy products to boot.

In 1946, Massey-Harris, which later became Massey-Ferguson, started to produce tractors and combine harvesters in a factory just outside the town. And of course, I must not forget Johnnie Walker's whisky factory on Hill Street opposite Kilmarnock Infirmary. The aroma of whisky permeated the air around the factory and I could often smell it years later when I worked in the infirmary.

John's father, who was a farmer, died in 1819. Consequently, the farm was sold, and John bought himself a grocer's shop in Kilmarnock. He turned out to be an excellent businessman, especially when it came to whisky. At that time, most businesses sold single malt whisky, but John began to blend them together, providing a consistently good whisky every time. When he passed away in 1857 his prosperous business passed to his son, Alexander. The railway had arrived in Kilmarnock by that time, allowing goods to be transported throughout the country, and onto cargo ships to be sent around the world. In 1867, Alexander produced Johnnie Walker's first unique and commercial blend, calling it 'Old Highland Whisky'. With a stroke of genius, Alexander employed ship's captains as agents to take his whisky around the globe; he also introduced a square bottle to help prevent breakages, adding a distinctive label which was put onto the bottles at twenty-four degrees to make it stand out further from other brands.

Alexander left the company to his sons, Alexander, a master blender, and George, in 1889. They renamed a new range of whiskies – Johnnie Walker Red Label and Johnnie Walker Black Label. Over lunch one day, illustrator Tom Browne sketched a logo of a 'Striding Man' on the back of a menu. Alexander and George loved it and the rest, as the saying goes, is history!

The people of Kilmarnock have always been proud of the fact that the first collection of works and poems by Robert Burns was published as *The Kilmarnock Volume* in 1786, but of course, that had no impact in the town in the 1950s and 60s. Industry was the name of the game and there was certainly plenty to choose from. Kilmarnock was indeed a hub of prosperous industry.

My mother was petite, blonde, slim and attractive. She worked in the Crown Wallpaper shop in Titchfield Street when she first met Dad, and then moved to Brighter Homes in West George Street. Both shops sold quality wallpapers and paints, and Mum insisted on only the best quality wall coverings when it came to decorating our family home. When I was about five or six, Mum would take me into the town on a Saturday. I loved the hustle and bustle of King Street in Kilmarnock. It was always teeming with shoppers, usually dressed in their Saturday best. People stopped on the street to chat and catch up with each other. Going to the shops on a Saturday without getting changed into your best attire was unheard of. I often had a coat with hat to match in the winter, or a summer dress with white cardigan and a white straw hat in the summer, which I also wore to Sunday school every week (I have certificates and books to prove it).

My brother Jim was born when I was six. By all accounts he was a perfect baby, and I loved to help look after him. I watched intently as Mum measured out his Ostermilk formula and added the cooled boiled water for his feed and felt very pleased with myself when he would fall asleep in my arms after I fed him from his bottle. His cot was in my room, and as he grew so did his love of orange juice. He would wallop his bottle off the cot sides (so much so that Mum swapped his glass bottle for a plastic one), and shouted, 'Dooce Caggy, dooce Caggy!' He hadn't quite mastered the words 'juice' and 'Jacqueline' and so it was 'dooce' and 'Caggy'.

One of my earliest memories is of walking from our home in Gatehead Road to my gran and papa's home in Woodbank Road when I was about three years old. How that came about I have no idea; quite a feat for a small child to walk the length and breadth of the village, crossing roads to boot. I remember knocking on the imposing, green, wooden back door to the house and nobody answering. I have since discovered that Gran and Papa, who were having breakfast with Uncle Jim and Aunt Bette Manderson at the time, thought they had heard something and looked out of the window but couldn't see anything. Well they wouldn't, I was knee high to a daisy at that time. When they eventually did grasp that I was there and opened the door, I apparently said matter-of-factly that I had been wearying to see my gran and papa. Another memory I have about 35 Woodbank Road is getting locked in the toilet on numerous occasions. My Uncle Robert had to climb up and pull himself through the narrow bathroom window to rescue me. Rapunzel, eat your heart out! He has never let me live it down.

We lived in the village of Crosshouse, which is situated just outside Kilmarnock, so going into town meant a ride on a bus. Mum and Dad had lived at 81 John Finnie Street in Kilmarnock when they were first married. I think Mum found village life rather strange after living in the town all her life. That said, we were very fortunate to have a car at the time, but Mum couldn't drive. Dad had tried to teach her once on an airfield, but apparently, she made a beeline for the only aircraft in sight, so he gave up. Mum preferred the blue A1 buses and would often let a red 'Western' bus pass by if it arrived first. Much to my intense disappointment we always sat downstairs. The smokers always went upstairs; both my parents were non-smokers and hated the smell of cigarette smoke.

I watched intently as the bus conductress ding-dinged the bell to let the driver know when to stop and go. The older buses had a wire running just below the ceiling which was pulled twice by the conductress to ring the bell; the newer ones had a shiny metal disc with a red button in the middle. She (I say 'she' quite deliberately, there were very few conductors on that bus route, and all bus drivers, without exception were male), bustled around, collecting fares in her smart, crisply ironed uniform and polished leather money bag. I particularly enjoyed watching her use the ticket machine. It made an appealing whirring sound as it produced a printed ticket. I cannot describe the excitement I felt if the conductress needed to change the ticket roll, and the anxiety if there were other children on the bus. Occasionally, I would be the chosen one, the one who got the remainder of the old roll to take home; that small roll of paper tickets provided endless fun on our staircase, where I would strategically place teddy bears and toys, making sure plenty of them were upstairs. At that time, we had a patterned red hall and stair carpet, from BMK, of course. Held in place with stair rods, the edges of the steps were shiny with gloss white paint. Mum would polish the painted edges with Min cream polish once a week, probably to get rid of the marks I made, until they shone. It was very important to me that when climbing the stairs of my *bus* that I only used the painted part of each step for some reason. I would hang onto the bannister for dear life to avoid walking on the carpet and slipping on the polished painted surface. I would ask Mum for some loose change which went into one small handbag which I wore crisscrossed over another which acted as my ticket machine. Our front door had brass tubular bells next to it which I would ping against the wall as my very own bus bell.

Mum loved D.M. Hannah's grocer shop located on Portland Street; it had a wonderful selection of cheese, all sorts of cold meats, row upon row of jars containing jewel-coloured jams, marmalades, curds and chutneys. It had a long, polished wooden counter. We would wait patiently, taking in all the sights and delicious smells of coffee, tea and spices. I seem to remember that there was always a queue. The staff were friendly and polite and pristinely dressed. Mum would ask for half a pound of cheese, a quarter pound of gammon etc. and it would be weighed, measured and carefully wrapped by hand in paper… not a plastic bag in sight.

Then we would make our way to McGarrity's the butcher. I didn't like this shop much; the smell of raw meat was overpowering for me. There was a copious amount of sawdust on the floor and animal carcasses hanging helplessly from hooks in the ceiling. They looked nothing like farm animals to me, but then, they did not look remotely like anything served up for dinner on a plate either. Again, we would queue, Mum would place her order and listen to suggestions from the butcher. The butcher always wore a white overall, striped apron and hat. Often the owner would wear a bow tie. McGarrity's mince rounds, fresh from the oven with their crisp golden pastry on top were particularly difficult to resist especially when the olfactory nerve had kicked in. The meat was wrapped in greaseproof paper, put into a paper bag and the butcher would write the price on it using a thick pencil which was usually kept tucked behind his ear. The money was always taken by a cashier in a separate booth, never handled by the butcher.

Then came my favourite part. A trip to Lauders department store in King Street for lunch. Lauders was originally built in 1864 but was destroyed by a fire in 1923. It was rebuilt and renamed as Lauders Emporium. There was also Lauders the bakers, which was opened by another branch of the Lauder family in 1869, and Lauders the ironmongers. I believe there was Lauders the Hatters in the town around 1900, but I don't remember hearing anyone in my family mention it.

I enjoyed going into the ironmongers, it had industrial-looking wooden floors, a huge assortment of brushes, brooms and dustbins pots and pans, and a wonderful smell of paraffin, candlewax and mothballs. (I remember Mum keeping a supply of mothballs and fire lighters in the pocket of her smock top to sniff at every opportunity when she was pregnant with Jim and Alastair.)

Lauders department store was the biggest shop on King Street. It had a restaurant on the top floor and we used the lift to get to it, the only one in the town if I remember correctly. I enjoyed going in the lift, it was the old-fashioned type with a metal trellis door, and it had windows which allowed you to see around the store as you travelled up and down. I remember it was usually operated by a very small man with dark, Brylcreemed hair who wore built-up, shiny black shoes which fascinated me.

The restaurant/tea room was on the top floor. The waitresses wore black dresses, white aprons and frilly caps. On arrival, you were greeted promptly and politely, and usually asked to wait to be seated. It was always busy. There were numerous tables dressed in pure white linen tablecloths and napkins which were so thick that they were difficult to fold. The most popular tables were at the back of the room which was the front of the store and overlooked King Street and the throngs of shoppers and the traffic. The silver cutlery seemed very heavy to me, and I was enthralled by the silver cake and sandwich stands which offered no end of delicious-looking food to eat. It felt very special and grown up, and I was always on my best behaviour. The silver tea pots were too heavy for me to lift, but I was usually allowed to fill the tea pot up using the smaller hot water jug when we were ready for more tea. I loved these outings. If I was good, occasionally I would get to choose a small toy or a comic such as *Bimbo* or the *Bunty* to take home (progressing a few years later to *The Mandy, Princess Tina* and *Jackie*). A favourite choice was a book with a cardboard dress-up doll, which had an assortment of cut-out clothes, or a small blackboard with a wooden frame and a packet of chalk and then I would play at 'schools' for hours on end. It was great when Jim came along and was old enough to be my pupil (whether he liked it or not is a different matter altogether).

Figure 3: *Jim and Alice circa 1956*

Figure 4: *My lovely mum and dad*

Arriving back home, we would find Dad watching the football results or the wrestling, the coal fire would be blazing, and the living room looked cosy. William Hartnell was Doctor Who around that time, and in 1966 the Cybermen arrived on our screens. The Cybermen absolutely terrified me, causing me to adopt a rather unusual method of getting to bed. I can remember that there was a coffee table against the right-hand wall as I entered my bedroom. It had been in the living room, but the glass top was broken so it was relegated to my room. I would climb on top of the polished wooden table, walk along the length of it to reach the fireplace. Then I would hop down onto the hearth, taking care not to slip on the shiny beige tiles. From there I could launch myself onto my bed and hide under the covers just in case there was a Cyberman hiding underneath the bed! The coffee table also made an excellent stage for me and my friends to put on shows, just as the coal bunker in the back garden was used in games of 'Batman' owing to its proximity to the metal clothes pole which allowed us to slide down it to our imaginary bat mobile.

I would often watch 'The Man from U.N.C.L.E.', acronym for the fictional American, United Network Command for Law Enforcement, and Top of The Pops on a Thursday night with my friend Erica and her sister Karen. They had a pink tiled staircase in their house which had a white rubber trim. It was lovely, and I had not seen anything like it before, but we were well warned by Mrs. Smith not to leave footprints on it. They had a separate sitting room which housed the television set which meant we could dance around uninhibited, to the pop tunes of the day without being watched by grownups. The Man from U.N.C.L.E. looked very glamorous; the characters had names like Napoleon Solo, and Ilya Kuryakin, played by Robert Vaughn and David McCallum respectively. I especially loved it when April Dancer, played by Stephanie Powers, the girl from U.N.C.L.E. was in it.

Mum always kept my hair short, I was a regular at Morgenthaler's hairdressers in John Finnie Street in Kilmarnock, and oh how I envied girls with long hair, but the ladies on television shows with their beehive and flip hairstyles were in another league altogether.

I collected pictures of horses and ballet dancers whenever I could and stuck them to my bedroom wall above the fireplace. At that particular time my wallpaper was primarily white and pink with cute kittens and balls of wool on it, I have no doubt that it was chosen by my mum and that it would have taken her ages to choose it. For Mum, choosing wallpaper was a very serious business and the final decision was not to be taken lightly.

A much-loved television programme was 'Blue Peter' – I watched it twice a week at five o'clock, straight after 'Jackanory', on Mondays and Thursdays. I wanted to make everything they suggested and pestered Mum for empty Fairy Liquid washing up detergent bottles and cardboard tubes from toilet rolls, and I could never understand why sticky-backed plastic was so hard to come by in Kilmarnock when they had copious amounts on Blue Peter. When I first started watching the programme it was presented by Christopher Trace and Valerie Singleton. John Noakes joined the team in 1965; he was my favourite because he was funny and a bit of a daredevil, plus I liked his friendly Yorkshire accent. I remember Petra the Blue Peter dog and just recently found out that the original Petra died of distemper when she was a puppy, but the programme's editor, Biddy Baxter, decided to find a suitable replacement rather than announce it and risk upsetting all the children who watched. Wise decision, if you ask me. One thing I wanted more than anything was a Blue Peter badge. Each presenter wore one, and every viewer who appeared on the programme was given a badge. There were various levels awarded from anything to submitting a letter or poem, to getting a gold badge for exceptional achievement. I had noticed that most children who appeared were from London, or at least England, which seemed like a far-off foreign land to my five-year-old self, so I felt that appearing on the programme was extremely unlikely for me. I watched with bated breath every week when they were running an appeal.

In 1964, Blue Peter viewers collected silver paper to buy a guide dog for the blind; in 1965, old wool was collected to purchase a tractor for a farm in Uganda; paperback books for an inshore lifeboat in 1966 (I struggled with this one because I loved all my books and read them over and over again) and we collected used stamps to raise money to convert four houses into flats for homeless families in 1967. I am still using 'we', because I really felt like I was a part of the show and made a difference. Each week the presenters would stand in front of the 'Blue Peter totaliser' and report our progress. It was incredible and emotional to watch when the target was reached, and work began in earnest to make that year's goal a reality, just from collecting scraps.

At school, we could also feel like we were helping a good cause and working towards a badge by collecting rosehips. During World War Two food rationing, it was recognised that rosehips could provide vitamins E, A, D and C. There were concerns about vitamin C because oranges were scarce. Britain could not import citrus fruits during wartime, and even after the war, citrus fruits were rationed and in short supply. The Women's Institute was asked to collect rosehips, as were other voluntary organisations. The rosehips were then used to make rosehip syrup, thought to be a rich source of vitamin C and therefore a good substitute. A rosehip collectors club was established in the 1950s. It was a nationwide scheme whereby children were organised locally, often at school, to forage for and collect wild rosehips which was great fun. Often on a nice day, our teacher would suggest a walk down to Laigh Milton Mill, a winding country road which led to the river and the mill, and we would pick rosehips plus other interesting finds for the class nature table. From the school the rosehips were taken to receiving depots and bought for 3d (three old pennies) or 4d per pound. We children were awarded badges for our efforts. One of the most well-known companies was Delrosa. The bottles of syrup were distributed free of charge to mothers for babies and children. This scheme lasted well into the 1960s. I can remember Mum coming home from the baby clinic after Jim was born with bottles of the sweet pink syrup, Ostermilk formula, which I thought had a horrible smell, and orange juice concentrate – a thick, gloopy, bright orange liquid which tasted amazing. I think it was still being distributed in 1969 when Alastair was born but I can't be sure.

Another thing which sticks in my mind around that time is the regular visit from the rag man. Every so often, I would hear the familiar bell ringing and horn honking and plead with Mum to look for some old clothes. I would then rush out and swap them for a balloon or maybe a pair of wonky sunglasses which made me feel like I was dizzy and walking down a slope. The rag man always seemed to be a bit rough and smelly, so I was always glad when the exchange had taken place and I could get back inside with my treasure. Needless to say, he didn't get any woollen items during 1965!

*

In 1967, both my maternal grandparents passed away within months of each other. Grannie, Christina Yuill Ramsay, who was born in 1903, was sixty-four, and Grampa, Alexander Brownlee Lochlon, was fifty-eight. Sadly, I don't remember much about my grandparents, other than Grampa being very gentle and kind. He had tuberculosis (TB) and did not keep in good health. Because of Grampa's TB I was vaccinated with Bacillus Calmette-Guerin, BCG, against the disease when I was about eight years old and I seem to remember the blister at the vaccination site took weeks to heal properly and I was not allowed to go swimming until it was completely dry and clean.

Of course, this meant that when we were given the Heaf diagnostic test, named after F. R. G. Heaf, in school aged about twelve, to see if we had been exposed to tuberculosis, mine was positive. It was also known as the Sterneedle test and was administered by a Heaf gun which was a spring-loaded contraption which had six needles in circular formation. In school we referred to it as the dreaded six-needle jag, but because I had a positive result it meant that I did not require another BCG vaccination and felt quite relieved about that and proudly showed off my bright red six-needle pattern on my arm to anyone who was remotely interested in what seemed like months. The Heaf test was discontinued in 2005 when the Mantoux test took over.

My grannie died in Kilmarnock Infirmary; she had a perforated bowel and the cause of her death was recorded as peritonitis. Mum remembers a very kind, gentle and softly spoken nurse looking after Grannie, her name was Nurse Mackenzie, she came from the small island of Benbecula in the Outer Hebrides. I was to know her in the future as Sister Luney; she was extremely strict and ran her female surgical ward with regimental precision. The softer she spoke the deeper the trouble you were in and she frightened the life out of me.

I do remember spending time with Grannie and Grampa during my summer school holidays. I slept in what seemed like a very high, huge bed with a pink shiny quilt on it. Grannie would place chairs at the sides to stop me from falling out of it in the night. They had lots of sweet-scented pink roses in the garden. Whenever I smell roses like that today, I am transported back to that time.

Grannie was a small woman, often known as 'Teeny'. By all accounts, she was a force to be reckoned with. She used to grate an apple for me and sprinkle it with sugar. I loved it, and it just didn't taste the same when Mum did it.

Grampa was quite tall and had snowy white hair. He was a quiet, mild-mannered man and he smiled a lot. One memory which sticks out was when Grannie and Grampa bought a new budgerigar. He was green. I was told that I could choose a name for the new feathered friend, and promptly chose Ringo, after my favourite Beatle.

Ringo came to live with us after Grannie and Grampa passed away. The budgie, that is, not the drummer!

CHAPTER 2

MY MUM AND DAD

"Family is not an important thing. It is everything."

- Michael J Fox

Dad was born on the 8th of April 1938, in Finlay's building, which was on Gatehead Road in Crosshouse. He was the first of three children born to Margaret and James Heron, my beloved gran and papa. He was the first grandchild for my paternal great-grandmother and great-grandfather so, consequently, was a bit spoiled by his granny and 'Granta' as he was known.

My grandmother remembers that their flat in Finlay's buildings had an abundance of cockroaches because of the heat from bakery downstairs. She also told me about proudly showing Dad off to neighbours just after he was born and one woman saying to her, 'You wullnay rear that wean hen,' meaning that he (Dad) would die in infancy.

Apparently, he was quite a small, frail-looking baby and had a twisted foot. The doctor suggested callipers may be required, but my gran's brother, who was a physiotherapist, said that was nonsense and that Gran should massage Dad's foot with oil every day and he demonstrated how it should be done. Dad is now eighty and going strong, and still walks as straight as the soldier he became, never having needed callipers. So, Uncle John Durnie was correct. Dad eventually got a brother, Tom and a sister, Margaret.

Gran and Papa lived at 15 Annandale Crescent during the war and later moved to a brand-new house at 35 Woodbank Road.

Gran and Papa often told me that my dad and Uncle Tom were very mischievous and were always getting into trouble. One story Gran loved to recall was the Christmas she had been saving up her wartime food rations and had managed to get hold of half a Christmas cake and some other luxuries. The sideboard only locked at one side, but she was sure the boys would not work out how to get to the carefully stored and precious foodstuff via the other door. They did. Not only that, they had picked all the royal icing and marzipan off the cake. My Uncle Tom also bored a hole in the bottom of a can of condensed milk which was in the pantry so that both boys could sup the sweet contents. Gran kept checking to see that it was still there, happy when she saw it intact on the pantry shelf. When she picked up the tin to use it, her hand flew ceilingward because the can was empty. Neither brother would tell on the other so they both got 'leathered' with the strap kept for that purpose!

Dad can remember visiting his granny who lived in the nearby village of Springside and would regularly walk with his Auntie Agnes (my papa's sister) to nearby Drybridge to watch WWII aircraft landing and taking off. Very exciting for a small boy. Grannie and Granta lived in what were known as The Six Rows, miners' cottages in the village. My great-grandfather was a ploughman, but some family members seem to recall that he had also worked at the pit head of the local coal mine at one time. Most of the houses in the six rows were two apartments (one bedroom, one living room dwellings). They were very unusual in that the toilets and washhouses with their copper boilers, were in front of the houses and not at the back. My Aunt Margaret, who is only sixteen years older than me, can remember carrying water into the house from the well at the front of the house using a pail. Waste water was carried out to the cesspool which was also at the front of the house. She can also vaguely recollect a small boy falling into the boiler one wash day, but this was hushed up and not spoken about in front of other children.

By all accounts Dad was well thought of at Crosshouse Junior Secondary School. He started school aged five. He was in the football team and (whisper it) the Scottish country dancing team and was a prefect when he left school aged fifteen.

Dad started work as an office boy at Scottish Aviation in 1953, moving on to his apprenticeship as a maintenance electrician in 1954 which he completed in 1959.

Mum and Dad first met in the Western SMT bus station in Portland Street, Kilmarnock (I think that was in 1955). They were introduced to each other by a mutual friend. At that time, Mum, Alice Isabella Lochlon, lived at 11 Fleming Street in Riccarton, Kilmarnock, with her sister Betty, and my grannie and grandpa. The buildings have now been demolished, as has Mum's old school, The Glencairn School. I recall walking through Kilmarnock down towards Riccarton to see the school for myself with one of my friends when I was about ten years old. Quite a distance from Crosshouse. I hasten to add, I did not tell anyone I was going, or in fact that I had been; the freedom we had to roam around then is almost inconceivable these days, but I knew I would have been told off for venturing so far on my own.

Mum has many happy memories of life in the red sandstone tenement building she grew up in, with its black leaded stove and outside wash house that could be used once a week by each household. My granny's day was a Tuesday. The family lived with Grannie Ramsay, Mum's maternal grandmother, who lived until she was ninety years old. They were visited frequently by aunts, uncles and cousins to chat, catch up, play cards and dominos. They often enjoyed singing. Mum's Aunt Alice had a beautiful singing voice and played the piano.

Mum and Auntie Betty would buy their comics and Enid Blyton books from Tam Bell's paper shop. Occasionally they would be sent to Mintos Fish and Chip Shop armed with an ashet (white metal dish piped with blue) and a clean tea towel to cover the dish to keep the chips warm, Apparently, lots 'disappeared' on the journey home.

Both girls attended Riccarton Sunday School and remember having lots of parties and days out.

The family did lots of walking at the weekends and went to the Forum Cinema every weekend and for a treat, they would have Forum Café ice cream. The Forum Café is still going strong to this day; I think it is the best ice cream I have ever tasted!

Figure 5: *Dad, front row second from left*

Figure 6: *Little Alice!*

Figure 7: *Mum is the blonde in the middle of the picture looking to her right.*
Taken on Coronation Day

My parents eventually married in 1959. Dad was called up for National Service on the 18th of January 1960. Dad served two years as a Royal Highland Fusilier, RHF, which he did not want to do but ended up loving military life and excelling in all aspects of it.

He was awarded a silver rose bowl for being The Best All-Round Recruit and made a film for the regiment which was shown on a popular lunchtime show on Scottish television called 'The One O'Clock Gang'. We have tried to locate this film but have not been able to, which is unfortunate, not least because since he was on draft to go to Aden, Dorothy Paul sang 'Goodbye Jimmy Goodbye' to him.

As it turned out he was not sent to Aden and he worked for Major Gordon Pender who was his Commanding Officer. He was promoted to Lance Corporal and was sent on a Non-Commissioned Officer course which he passed with the highest possible marks. He was qualified to teach small arms and drill instruction. On returning to the depot he was immediately promoted to Full Corporal, two stripes fully substantive, and was senior to many of the regular Non-Commissioned Officers.

Major Pender was bitterly disappointed when Dad went against his advice and decided not to sign up and take a commission. They remained friends and kept in touch with each other until Major Pender, who had by now become a Colonel, died. Dad was delighted to receive an invitation to Colonel and Mrs. Pender's only daughter's wedding. Mum and Dad kept in touch with Debbie and her son for many years. During his time in the RHF Dad met his good friends Stewart Roxburgh and Willie Shaw who became a Major. Sadly both have passed away. I firmly believe that Dad would easily have made Major, if not beyond, and that it was a great pity that he returned to Scottish Aviation on January 18th 1962 to resume his trade. I expect he thought it was best for Mum and me.

In 1964, he joined the Coal Board and worked at Prestwick and Luger workshops, and then Daniel Construction in 1965 for a couple of years before returning to Scottish Aviation Ltd.

My dad worked extremely hard and took any overtime that was going. He worked until ten o'clock every Wednesday night. Often, he would often bring home mushrooms, picked from the side of the runway at Prestwick Airport in spite of being told off by someone in the control tower for doing it! Mum was always a bit suspicious of the fungi, but she would fry them in butter to accompany his traditional Wednesday night supper of eggs and steak.

Dad taught me to drive which had its ups and downs as you might imagine. Papa eventually got me an Austin 1100 (at least I think that was what it was) to learn to drive in, to save the gearbox in Dad's adored Ford Escort Sports car. OAG 791L, that is the only car registration I have ever remembered (partly because it was hanging on my brother Jim's bed in Crosshouse hospital for several weeks after he had a nasty accident whilst driving the Escort).

I wasn't allowed to keep the car after I passed my test, much to my disappointment. It was purely on loan to me and was sold on.

Figure 8: *Dad, second from right. Guard of Honour for Princess Margaret, who failed to show up!*

Mum was a typical 1960s housewife. She kept the house clean and tidy and went shopping almost every day with her trusty message bag. We were served by numerous mobile shops at that time. I can remember being sent out to buy bread (and sometimes cakes) from Girdwood's van, and for half a stone of Ayrshire potatoes and a pound or two of apples amongst other things from Andrew Macindoe's fruit and vegetable van. Milk was delivered to our doorstep by Wullie Tannock and we would sometimes order orange juice from him too. My favourite was Bramante's ice cream van. Often on a Sunday I would go out with a bowl and ask for it to be filled with ice cream topped with raspberry sauce.

At that time, Crosshouse had a Co-operative grocery store simply known as The Store, a Co-op bakery, butchers, and drapery, as well as a small general store known locally as 'Broons'. It had previously been known as Carmel Stores owing to its location on the bridge over Carmel Water. Broons was very popular with school children. It tempted us with lucky bags, penny chews and trays stuffed with pocket money sweets, Parma violets, gob stoppers, McCowan's toffee bars, black jacks, fruit salad, flying saucers and liquorice fountains to name but a few. The shop assistants waited patiently while kids of all ages decided how to spend their tuck shop money. I am sure they would have sighed with relief when the afternoon bell rang to start lessons again. The village also had a fish and chip shop referred to simply as Geordie's, owned by George Biagie, a barber, a hairdresser and an off-license, a bookmaker and of course a post office. There were also two public houses, 'The Tap' pub, and 'The Bottom' pub which is one of the oldest buildings in Crosshouse, built sometime before 1855. It is a children's nursery at the time of writing this. What had once been the local school, built in 1848 with an adjoining teachers' house, was now used as a community centre. The village library was located at the back of the community centre, I remember it being run by a lovely tall lady called Madge. I spent many happy hours in that library.

I always came home from school at lunchtime, even when I moved from Crosshouse Primary School to Grange Academy in Kilmarnock. This involved running from the back entrance of Grange Academy, up through Annanhill estate to the bus stop. Lunch would usually be ready and waiting, prepared by Mum. I just had enough time to eat it, usually a sandwich, empty my school bag of the morning's books and jotters and fill it with the ones required for the afternoon lessons. If I had managed to catch the early bus, there was even time to watch a bit of Pebble Mill at One on BBC1 which was shown on weekdays at lunch time. All too soon it was time to run for a bus to take me back to Kilmarnock and the walk up Beech Avenue back to The Grange.

Mum would often make big steaming pots of lentil soup, potato soup or chicken broth using the carcass from our Sunday roast (frozen) chicken. It was always a rush between me and my brothers to see who would be first to get the thick end slice from the plain Mother's Pride loaf which we preferred to a pan loaf when it came to soup dunking.

In the evenings, we would have apple crumble, eve's pudding or rice pudding, not every day but quite often. My favourite part of the rice pudding was the golden skin on the top where Mum had daubed knobs of butter on it before baking it in the oven.

Often, after our Sunday dinner, Mum would make strawberry flan. A light sponge flan case filled with strawberries, jelly and topped with cream. I absolutely loved it. Other times it would simply be tinned fruit salad with Carnation milk poured over it. I requested a strawberry flan when I came out of hospital after having my tonsils and adenoids removed in 1969 in Seafield Hospital in Ayr, which turned out to be quite a traumatic experience for me.

I was one of the oldest children on the ward. Most were toddlers. From my bed, which was right by the door, I could see the other children being taken to theatre along the dark, wood-panelled, galleried corridor, and being brought back again, semi-conscious and crying, with congealed blood on their pillows. Now, I will admit it may not have been as bad as I am describing, but that is certainly how it looked through my nine-year-old eyes! I lay there, terrified, waiting for my turn.

Although it was a children's hospital, it was not like the child-friendly paediatric hospitals we have today. There were certainly no cartoon tabards for the nurses to wear, or colourful, artwork that I can remember. Most of the nurses were lovely, but many seemed to prefer the toddlers and fussed over them, leaving me to my own devices.

I vividly remember arriving in the pungent operating theatre and having what seemed like a massive black smelly mask plonked onto my face and then a feeling of being sucked into it like it was some sort of vacuum cleaner.

To this day, I cannot stand having a mask on my face and chose an analgesia-free childbirth rather than endure gas and air through a face mask, but I digress.

Post-operatively I filled bowl after stainless steel bowl with bloody liquid. I vomited blood to such an extent that I could no longer sit up on my own but seem to remember being told off for slumping over on my bed and for making a mess of the bed sheets.

I ended up back in the operating theatre to have my wounds cauterised. That, I thankfully do not remember. I found myself back in bed with a cannula taped to my small arm receiving a pint of someone else's blood. Thank you, whoever you were!

Dad came to visit me every night. I was kept in longer than everyone else because of the complications. Mum was expecting Alastair at that time; I don't remember her ever coming to visit, maybe she was advised not to.

It was Easter time and a local minister came to visit us and handed out Cadbury's Creme Eggs. They were confiscated by the nursing staff and we never saw them again. These things are very important when you are nine.

Needless to say, it can't have been all that bad, because one of the first things I wanted when I got home to rest and recuperate was a nurse's outfit. I can remember playing endless games of hospitals using toys and my ever-suffering little brother Jim. I can honestly say, that this was when the seed was sewn. I didn't realise it at the time, but I had found my calling.

Although I remember Seafield as an imposing and intimidating building for sick children, I can now admire and esteem such a wonderful building which sadly has been abandoned and allowed to decay. That said, I believe plans are afoot to convert the old hospital into flats.

It was designed and built by Sir William Arrol in 1887. Sir William was a Civil Engineer who had been contracted to build a replacement for the Tay bridge following the disaster which happened on Sunday the 28th of December 1879 on the Edinburgh to Aberdeen line. The bridge which had only been standing for about a year, collapsed while a train was crossing over it during a violent storm. There were more than ninety victims although only forty-six bodies were ever recovered.

William Topaz McGonigal (his books remain in print today, but he was once known as the worst poet who wrote in the English language – his audiences even threw rotten fish at him whilst he read aloud) penned a poem about the disaster. Here is an excerpt:

Beautiful Railway Bridge of the Silv'ry Tay!
Alas! I am very sorry to say
That ninety lives have been taken away
On the last Sabbath day of 1879,
Which will be remember'd for a very long time.

'Twas about seven o'clock at night,
And the wind it blew with all its might,
And the rain came pouring down,
And the dark clouds seemed to frown,
And the Demon of the air seem'd to say --
"I'll blow down the Bridge of Tay."

I must now conclude my lay
By telling the world fearlessly without least dismay,
That your central girders would not have given way,
At least many sensible men do say,
Had they been supported on each side with buttresses,
At least many sensible men confesses,
For the stronger we our houses do build,
The less chance we have of being killed.

Sir William Arrol also won the contract to build the Forth Rail Bridge (1883-1890), and was additionally preparing to build Tower Bridge in London.

He acquired the Seafield Estate, thus preventing it from being divided up into house-building plots. He pulled down the original, unexceptional mansion, and replaced it with an Italianate four-storey, yellow sandstone mansion, with beautiful wood panelling and ornate mosaic tile floors, complete with a vast conservatory and a supply of heated sea water for bathing, which at that time was revered and thought to be extremely therapeutic. The mansion also boasted a stunning library and housed a valuable art collection. It also had a striking hall, built with acoustics in mind for musical presentations.

Not bad for a boy, born in 1839, who was working in a cotton mill at the age of nine. William started training to be a blacksmith at the age of thirteen and, fortunately for the country, studied mechanics and hydraulics at night school. Sir William was responsible for the Nile Bridge in Egypt and the Hawkesbury Bridge in Australia. Plus, he built a gantry at the Harland and Wolff shipyards in Belfast, 'The Arrol Gantry' which was used in the construction of RMS *Titanic* and her sister ships.

He died at Seafield in 1913 and was inducted to the Scottish Engineers Hall of Fame in 2013. What an outstanding and noteworthy man; I sincerely hope that his mansion is once again put to good use with as many original features intact as possible.

CHAPTER 3

MY FAMILY – 1960S AND 70S

"Youth is wasted on the young."

- George Bernard Shaw

We lived at 26 Gatehead Road in Crosshouse. Up until I was about twelve, we had a large red three-piece suite in the living room, a coffee table and a black and white television set. I don't remember a time when we didn't have a family car. I also recall the excitement one weekend we went to the shops and bought a fridge AND a camera at the same time (using cash). Oh, the absolute joy of being able to drink cool milk. I am sure it made Mum's life a whole lot easier and meant she didn't need to visit the shops on a daily basis. At school, our daily bottle of milk was very popular in the winter when it was almost frozen, so long as the birds hadn't got to the milk crate first and pecked through the foil lids to get at the cream on top of the non-homogenised milk. A sea of small hands went flying into the air with great enthusiasm when the teacher asked who wanted seconds... not so much in the summer when the thick yellow cream had a distinctly cheesy aroma.

Speaking of bottles, there was untold joy if you found an empty lemonade bottle whilst you were out playing. There was a system of deposit refund on beverage bottles. Apparently, this scheme dates to the early twentieth century because the heavy glass bottles used for carbonated drinks were expensive to manufacture but were hardy enough to be re-filled and re-sold. To encourage customers to return them, the deposit refund was introduced. It didn't matter where the bottle had been bought, any shop which sold that brand would offer a refund. In fact, many charities used bottle collections to raise funds, but for me and my friends in the 1960s, it meant pennies for the sweetie shop, usually Broons, where as usual, we would take an absolute age choosing between a packet of spangles or a bar of Fry's Five Boy's chocolate. Finding or being given a bottle to return was especially useful when going to the ABC Cinema's Children's Matinee on a Saturday, commonly known as the ABC Minors. Me and a friend would travel, unaccompanied by an adult, by bus into Kilmarnock. I was about ten or eleven at the time. We would get off in John Finnie Street and, forgoing Broons, make straight for the sweetshop adjacent to the bus stop. I would usually choose between a quarter of sherbet lemons or sherbet strawberries, cola cubes or my favourite, chocolate limes, all of which would last for the duration of the films and were easy to eat in the dark. I can remember singing along to the song which was played every week. The lyrics were projected onto the cinema screen.

We are the boys and girls well known as Minors ABC

And every Saturday all line up to see the films and shout aloud with glee,

We like to laugh and have our sing song; such a happy crowd are we.

We're all pals together, we're the Minors of the ABC.

Happy days and frayed mouths.

Dad, who could turn his hand to most things, boxed in the kitchen, creating lots of storage space. The painted white cupboards had yellow Formica worktops and an undulated wood trim which was also painted white. We also had wooden stools with yellow padded seats. It looked very modern compared to some other kitchens at the time. Dad kept the two original large cupboards in the kitchen; one housed the hot water tank and immersion heater, pipes to hang clothes on to air and Mum's twin-tub washing machine; the other was filled with a hotchpotch of cleaning materials, shoe polish and dusters. Both were removed when the kitchen was refurbished again in the 1980s.

During the school holidays, television programmes were broadcast during the day. This was most unusual and exciting because apart from the test card and the odd school's programme there was nothing to watch in the day time. White Horses and Robinson Crusoe stick in my mind, I loved Laurel and Hardy which tended to be shown at Christmas time. 'Tales from Europe' was intriguing and unusual. I particularly remember one story called 'The Singing Ringing Tree'. You can still view it on You Tube.

As I got older, another favourite at Christmas time was 'The Morecambe and Wise Show', an absolute must see. It was, without fail, a talking point when we got back to school after the holidays, especially discussing the celebrity guests who were often seen doing things we could never have imagined them doing.

I used to spend a lot of time visiting Aunt Margaret, my dad's sister, during the school holidays. She lived at the other end of the village, and I would hop on my bike and cycle over there. She was and still is fun loving and full of beans and made me feel welcome. We had always been close; I was her flower girl when she married Uncle Robert. She and Uncle Robert were sometimes mistaken for my parents because they spent so much time with me when I was a baby and a toddler. I was also close to her two sons, my cousins Kevin and Scott, we enjoyed spending time together. I remember spending a week with Aunt Margaret, Kevin and Scott at Gran and Papa's caravan which was situated in New England Bay caravan site in Wigtownshire. It was a bittersweet time, in that Uncle Robert had gone ahead to Powell River in Canada to find a job and a house before sending for Auntie M and the boys. They were emigrating, and I was devastated. My papa was almost inconsolable, and it was left to Gran to be the one who stayed strong for everyone. It seemed so far away. In those days you had to book a time slot if you wanted to make a telephone call over the festive period. I wrote letter after letter after they moved to Canada and loved it when Gran and Papa went over to visit and came back with lots of photographs and news, not to mention cool presents. We regularly recorded our news onto cassette tapes to send too which seemed a good alternative to writing screeds on what had become all too familiar air mail writing paper. Oh, what we would have given for email or Skype, but the concept of both would have seemed impossible and pure fantasy to us then.

When I was fourteen, I went to work as a waitress/ chambermaid for George Hannah and his wife. George was our Prudential Insurance man, he came to collect Mum and Dad's weekly payment on a Saturday morning. He also owned a shop in Bank Street, Kilmarnock, which sold clothes and carpets and he later bought a beautiful guest house in Skelmorlie, just outside Largs. The front of the house overlooked the sea with uninterrupted views across the water to Arran; the back overlooked lush green hills.

George asked me to work in the guest house for the duration of the school summer holidays and asked if I knew of anyone else who would be interested in joining me. I jumped at the chance to be parent and brother free for a few weeks. He said I would work in the mornings, have the afternoons off but had to be back in time to help serve out the evening meals. I really enjoyed it but suffered from somewhat unexpected homesickness. Nevertheless, I loved the house and meeting the guests. My school friend, Elizabeth, came with me. We were asked to wear kilts when we were working in the dining room serving breakfasts and evening meals. I predominantly remember that Mrs. Hannah was a cordon bleu cook. She used ingredients I had never heard of before such as tarragon, the food tasted unfamiliar but delicious, and all her fried eggs were cooked in metal moulds and had to be perfectly round or they were rejected. Elizabeth and I never went short of fried eggs for breakfast. One day I would serve breakfast and Elizabeth would be chambermaid, then we would swap.

With every afternoon off, we would regularly spend time in Largs or get the ferry to Rothesay which was quite a novelty. We became regulars and never tired of it. I am sure Caledonian Macbrayne (Cal. Mac.) profits soared that year.

George got quite excited one morning and insisted that we gather in front of the house to look out to sea. There was a large boat sailing by, it looked very majestic and I had not seen one like it on the Ayrshire coastline before. George was more than a little disappointed when we failed to recognise it as the Royal Yacht *Britannia*.

Around this time, I was a member of the school hill-walking club and badminton club.

In 1973, I was given a Yoney Yama (which eventually became 'Yanex') badminton racket for Christmas. I totally loved it and it was much admired at school and at Crosshouse badminton club. (and by my dad who also liked to play). I thought it was the best present ever until I got a much-coveted cassette recorder in 1974. I became quite adept at recording the top twenty hits from the radio on a Sunday evening, managing to stop recording before the DJ started to speak thus ruining the whole effect. I have a vivid memory of fusing all the lights in the house during one recording because I twirled my basket-style light shade a tad too far in an attempt to make disco-like patterns on my bedroom wall, causing the cable protruding from the ceiling to snap in a puff of black smoke. Dad was far from amused.

Grange Academy had the use of a croft in Corrie on the beautiful Isle of Arran. A group of us from school would go for weekends, boarding the Cal. Mac. ferry in Ardrossan dressed in cagoules and carrying stuffed-to-the-gunnels rucksacks on our backs. I also wore a hat covered with badges of all kinds which I collected at that time, a favourite was a bright green frog. One time, a teacher even brought his golden Labrador, called Glen, along much to our delight.

The croft was situated at the base of Goat Fell (Gaelic – Gaoda Bheinn), in Corrie. The accommodation was typical bothy-come lodge with girls' and boys' dormitories, and communal living areas. We took it in turns to cook and clean up, which resulted in much hilarity and carrying on and a lot of barely edible food.

Before setting off on a walk, we would slather our boots with dubbing to keep our boots watertight. It rained quite often, but it didn't dampen our spirits.

I am very proud to say I got to see the stunning views from the top of Goat Fell, the highest point on the Isle of Arran at 874 metres (2,866ft). We also walked Caisteal Abhail, the most northerly of the four Arran Corbetts. This is known locally as 'The Sleeping Warrior' due to its outline as seen from the Ayrshire coastline. It has a jagged crevice, which is known as 'The Witches Step', which is where I tried abseiling for the first (and last) time.

Figure 9: *Village of Corrie, Isle of Arran*

The air was so pure and clean. Bubbling burns of clear sparkling water spilled and trickled southwards. We even drank some of it from cupped hands; it was freezing cold and thoroughly delicious.

The landscape is rugged and craggy, with areas of woodland, juniper trees and of course, purple heather, which reminds me: my English and American sons-in-law love finding ways to make me say purple, burger or, best of all murder, but that, as they say, is another story.

We were given access to the indoor pool at Blackwaterfoot, so basically, between the rain and the pool, we spent most of those weekends soaking wet.

I had an after-school job in Crosshouse Co-op. I worked on Thursdays, Fridays and on Saturday mornings. The shop was closed on Saturday afternoons. Those were the days.

I started by packing shelves, and eventually I was trusted enough to work on the Deli Counter. I loved using the bacon slicer and the cheese wire. Fridays were always busy at this counter because we took delivery of fresh fish which was very popular with the locals.

The store had fresh bread and rolls delivered every morning, carried on huge bread boards which the delivery man would balance on his shoulder. We would also take delivery of a selection of pies, tarts, iced buns referred to collectively as tea-bread, scones and potato scones to name but a few. These would quite literally sell like proverbial hot cakes.

Pat, the store manager, was a lovely man. He was keen for me to learn how to work in all areas of the shop. In typical managerial style, he was thinking ahead to the school holidays when I could work more hours and cover the regular staff holidays. So, I moved on to the tills, which I found very stressful. Mental arithmetic was and is not my strong point especially under pressure. The tills in those days did not tell you how much change was owed, and there were no bar codes to be scanned, prices were entered manually. I often got flustered by impatient customers who knew exactly how many Co-op dividend stamps to expect with their change and complained bitterly if there was one missing. If I remember correctly a full book of stamps provided the owner with 50p off their next shop. This may not sound like much, but at that time you could buy a gallon of petrol for 50p, so it was not to be sniffed at.

That said, the grocery tills were a doddle compared to the off-license, especially when Hogmanay, New Year's Eve, was approaching. Pat would assign me to the off-license deliberately saying it would be good practice for me. In the early seventies, it was predominantly men who bought alcohol from the shop. They would often flirt outrageously, adding embarrassment to the mix.

'Gimme a bottle of Red Label, a bottle of Smirnoff, and a bottle of Bacardi please, darlin', I've got fifty quid, so split what's left over evenly between cans of McEwan's Export and Pale Ale.'

My worst nightmare, and, what is more, we didn't use calculators.

Figure 10: *I was Crosshouse Gala Queen in 1972*

CHAPTER 4

I WANT TO BE A NURSE!

"Let us never consider ourselves finished nurses... we must be learning all of our lives."

- Florence Nightingale

I left school in the summer of 1977 and was glad to do so. I cannot agree with the person who said that school days are the best days of your life. I was fortunate to be offered full-time employment in the Co-op until I started nurse training at Ayrshire and Arran College of Nursing and Midwifery in February 1978.

Working in the Co-op was a happy time for me. My favourite part was receiving my brown paper pay packet with my name on it at the end of the week. What an amazing feeling, earning your own money for the first time was. Mum and Dad were very good to me. They didn't ask for dig money but expected me to save money and buy most of my own clothes, which I did.

I became close to the women who worked there. Betty Cannon, who was in the same age group as my gran, was so kind to me. She always called me Jackie, much to Gran's annoyance. Gran was always reminding people that my name was Jacqueline, not Jackie. Betty managed the drapery department which was situated at the entrance to the grocery store. The drapery had moved to the corner of Gatehead Road from its original premises on Irvine Road. The shop on Irvine Road was old-fashioned and had beautiful wooden counter tops and glass-fronted cabinets with drawer upon drawer of socks, handkerchiefs, thread, gloves etc. It also had a pneumatic tube system in place. Money taken from a customer after a sale was put into a container which was then transported along tubes to the cashier's office using suction similar to the way a vacuum cleaner works. Any change for the customer was returned in the same way. I loved watching the containers full of money and receipts zip along above my head before the store closed and was relocated.

Ina Faulds, who, like me, could turn her hand to anything required in the shop, was extremely funny and supportive, a laugh a minute with a genuine and warm personality. Margaret Murphy who had beautiful blonde bouffant hair, which later became a Joanna Lumley 'Purdy style' was married to John 'Spud' Murphy who was a professional football player, master of the sliding tackle, and part of the squad who defeated Rangers in 1975 (he was good friends with Alex Ferguson and has recently been indoctrinated into the Ayr United Hall of Fame). Margaret oversaw the cold meat and cheese counter. Anne Goldie who quietly and efficiently got on with the job in hand at the checkout was always helpful and unflappable. As a group, we made a staff Christmas dinner using the Baby Belling cooker in the back of the shop; again Pat would assign me to things which took me way outside of my comfort zone and for which I am extremely grateful. I made a steak pie for the first time in my life and the feeling of pride at being chosen to do so and about the final result stays with me to this day.

*

My family, especially my gran, were slightly surprised when I announced my intention to become a nurse. This was because, historically, I freaked out at the sight of my own blood after a fall. Apparently, I didn't cry when I fell over as many children did, but if I spied even a spot of blood on the injured part of my body it was all hell let loose.

I was interviewed at Ayrshire Central Hospital in Irvine, by Miss Cairns, who was the Senior Nursing Officer (the new term for Matron), at Kilmarnock Infirmary, and a few other health board officials. It seemed to go smoothly enough, but I wasn't holding my breath. Part of me would have been quite happy to stay at the Co-op and what I knew.

I got my letter of acceptance along with a date for my

Occupational Health check and list of vaccinations I would require. I was given an appointment to be measured for my uniforms, and asked whether I would require a room in the nurses' home at Ayrshire Central Hospital, where the College was located. I chose to remain at home and travel daily.

The letter also included a list of things I would need to buy including round-ended scissors, flat white shoes and a fob watch. It was getting very real, very real indeed.

The uniform was disappointingly plain and white, not at all like the ones worn by the nurses in Seafield Hospital in 1969. It had a round neck and short sleeves; trousers and tunics were not an option at that time. We wore flesh-coloured tights, although, as I got to be more senior and braver, I would buy a shade called chinchilla from Marks and Spencer's which was a brownish grey colour.

Becoming a student nurse meant quite a drop in salary; I barely made £90 per month to begin with, that was working at least forty hours per week; early shift 07:30 until 16:00, late shift 13:00 until 21:00, and night duty when called for. Nursing is not a profession where you can leave when your finish time comes around, you were expected to stay if required and we did without question.

I worked most weekends. We often had to work a ten-day stretch either before or after a long weekend off – Friday, Saturday, Sunday and Monday – but it usually seemed worth working ten days straight to have such a long time off. It was a learning curve and that curve was very steep. Nursing is a no-holds-barred vocation, and we were literally thrown in at the deep end after our eight weeks in college was over.

College itself was most enjoyable. Our class was made up of a lovely group of girls from many walks of life and from all over Scotland. We were taught basic nursing care, human anatomy and physiology, and practiced giving injections into a mattress, but the place where we really mastered our craft was on the wards. I can honestly say I learned something new every single day, and some things were quite shocking, alarming even, and often heartbreaking. That said, we had loads of lighter times and a great many laughs, camaraderie and fun.

Figure 11: *Kilmarnock Infirmary, nurses' home entrance at the northern end of Portland Street*

CHAPTER 5

KILMARNOCK INFIRMARY 1978-1981

"Cure sometimes, treat often, comfort always."

- Hippocrates

Kilmarnock Infirmary was originally opened in 1868 as Kilmarnock Fever Hospital. At that time, it had twenty-four beds, one matron and two nurses. Over the years it was extended to keep up with demand. In 1891, a children's block was added, plus a nurses' training school. Half of the monies required for these additional structures were provided by Lady Howard de Walden who resided at The Dean Castle. The other half was raised by local community fundraising.

When Kirklandside Hospital was completed in 1909, infectious cases were moved there, leaving just surgical and medical patients at the infirmary.

The largest extensions to Kilmarnock Infirmary were designed by Sir J.J. Burnet. He conferred with Doctor Mackintosh of The Western Infirmary in Glasgow. Built on raised ground, and boasting ornamental masonry, these additions made Kilmarnock Infirmary (KI) an imposing landmark in the town.

The first three-storey block was completed in 1915, creating fifty-seven beds; the second three-storey block was completed after the first world war in 1921. The original infirmary building was then used as the nurse's home.

During my time at Kilmarnock Infirmary, there were six wards, a casualty department, outpatient department, two theatres, a small pharmacy and x-ray. There was a mortuary in the basement, where else?

The nurses' home and administrative building was connected to the rest of the infirmary by a long, tiled corridor. There was no mistaking that you were in a hospital, it smelled strongly of disinfectant and surgical spirits. The floors were highly polished by the domestic staff in their maroon uniforms using large circular polishing machines.

Walking from the nurses' home, where we collected our uniforms from the laundry, towards the wards there was an imposing stone staircase on the left leading to what had been the old training school which now housed occupational health. Further along there was a corridor off to the right which led to the staff restaurant and kitchens. The restaurant was always busy, but we only had half an hour for lunch or dinner which included walking and queueing time, so it is little wonder that we often got indigestion from gulping down our food. It was even worse for smokers (which I tried for a while – sorry Dad) because you needed to fit in a nicotine fix too.

On leaving the restaurant, turning right, the first block you came to on the left-hand side housed ward six, male orthopaedic on the ground floor, ward four, female orthopaedic was on the second floor, and ward two female medical on the top floor. There was a large lift shaft just outside the entrance to ward six allowing access to wards four and two.

Next to that block midway between the ward blocks, was the theatre suite. There were two operating theatres, anaesthetic rooms, recovery room, and the usual autoclaves, sluices, male and female changing rooms and a small coffee room.

Compared to the rest of the building, the hospital smell in here was almost overwhelming. It clung to clothes left in your locker and to your hair even though hair was covered at all times by a theatre cap.

Beyond theatre on the left was the second three-storey block. Ward seven, male surgical on the ground floor, ward five (more about that later!), female surgical, gynae, and private patient rooms on the second floor, and ward three, male medical and the coronary care unit on the top floor.

There was an external walkway between ward five and ward four which we often used as a shortcut. This walkway also afforded a view of St Joseph's Church next door, and if you were lucky, the very handsome young priest would be in the grounds. We were much more used to older priests and ministers coming to visit the patients, so the tall dark Irishman was like a breath of fresh air and the fact that he was based next door was a bonus. I am sure that the biggest fascination was his unattainability!

There was also a lift shaft outside ward seven allowing access to wards five, three and the coronary care unit. There was another small staircase and another lift which led up to the main reception area, casualty, x-ray, outpatients, medical records and the main hospital entrance which was situated on Hill Street.

At that time, surgeons were exalted beings, and as a student nurse, you most definitely did not speak to one unless they spoke to you first, which they rarely did. This was much the same as was expected by anyone senior to you. As a first-year student with one blue stripe on your cap, you could get away with speaking to a second year with two stripes. You were expected to stick to third year students (with, yes, you've guessed it, three stripes) and pick their brains. Staff nurses, who had completed three years' training and passed their hospital and state finals, were generally much too grand to be bothered with first-year students. There may have been the odd exception to the rule but that is how I remember it. Sisters wore frilly starched caps and were almost in the same league as the surgeons as far as student nurses were concerned. If you got any attention from a Sister other than at appraisal time, it usually meant you were in trouble.

There were also pupil nurses who wore green stripes. They would qualify to be enrolled nurses after two years' training as opposed to a staff nurse after three years. They would often tease that it only took them two years to learn what took us three.

The auxiliary nurses, who wore grey uniforms and plain white caps, were by far the most helpful and approachable, and were generally every student or pupil nurse's best friend.

Most had been working on their allocated ward for many years, and what they didn't know about the daily running of it really wasn't worth knowing. They knew all of the Sisters' foibles, expectations, and most importantly moods.

KI had a senior nursing officer who wore a navy-blue uniform, and several nursing officers who wore a paler and rather waterier version of dress. Miss Harris sticks in my mind in that she terrified me. When she walked into the ward I would try to blend into the background and look as busy as possible so as not be noticed. You always knew when a nursing officer was approaching, because they wore shoes with a small heel which click-clacked expeditiously across the polished floor, unlike us rubber-soled minions.

Occasionally my strategy failed miserably, and I would be chosen to take her on a ward round. My fellow student and pupil nurses would gaze fleetingly in my direction, offering sympathy and support with their eyes, but with an unmistakable look of relief that they had not been selected.

During the ward round, we students and pupils were expected to know everything about every patient. Name, age, reason for admission, treatment, drugs, procedures, temperature, pulse, respirations, blood pressure, fluid balance, bowel movements and shoe size… Okay I lied about the shoe size.

The principal consultants during my time at KI were Doctor Barclay Barr, Medical Consultant. His registrar was Doctor Sheila Smith, a pleasant blonde lady. They were usually found in either ward two or three with Sisters Gibson and Ingles respectively.

The medical wards were always very busy. Like all the wards in the hospital, they were Nightingale wards with high ceilings and large bay windows. The medical wards often had beds down the middle offering the poor patients even less privacy than they would normally have in such an open-plan space. As a rule, new admissions to any ward were located nearest to the doors, and as they got better and ready for discharge they were moved up the ward towards the large bay windows.

Wards six and four, the orthopaedic wards, had a six-bed cot ward before you entered the main ward. Each bed could be seen easily from the duty room and again, the most vulnerable patients were located there. I remember being on night duty in ward four. A mother and her two daughters were admitted after a fatal road traffic accident. They had just arrived from America for a holiday. Dad was dead on arrival. Mum asked us to push the beds together so that she could hold hands with her girls. It was tragic, I will never forget that poor, unfortunate and lovely family.

Mr. Livingstone and Mr. Miller were the surgical consultants. Wards five and seven were male and female respectively. Ward five was run with military precision by Sister Nan Luney. Ward seven had Sister Auld at the helm.

Mr. Livingstone had a daughter who supposedly wanted to become a doctor. Astonishingly, Sister Luney would allow Miss Livingstone to accompany her father on ward rounds.

Day staff were expected on duty, dressed in full uniform, and ready for action at 07:30. The first thing we had to do was congregate in the duty room to listen to the report from the night staff. We would be informed of any admissions, which patients had required special attention, or anything untoward. We were also told about our duties for the morning and given any special instructions and information about the forthcoming day.

In ward five, if you arrived at 07:30 you had missed most of the report and received a brief but withering look from Sister Luney which I can only describe as haughty, self-satisfied annoyance. Sister Luney was always perfectly turned out and wore a pair of exalted, click-clackety shoes, the only Sister to do so. I was quite pleased about her choice of footwear, it meant I could hear her approaching and be on guard or, if at all possible, disappear, until she had gone again.

A standing joke was that a junior doctor allegedly once asked Sister Luney what was wrong with the patient's complexions, he thought that they all appeared to be sporting an unusual, dark, ruddy hue.

As the story goes, he then accredited the disorder to the fact that the patients' blankets had simply been tucked around them so firmly and tightly in order to make the ward look immaculate, that reduced blood circulation had ensued.

When I was a student nurse she terrified and intimidated me and did nothing to safeguard a glimmer of respect I may have held, when the tall ward television broke down during the Wimbledon men's finals. The nurses on duty decided to take a portable television from one of the empty private rooms so that the ladies could at least hear, if not actually see much of the tennis match. Sister insisted that the television set was returned to the empty private room it had been taken from. Even the patients dared not disobey her strict regime. It certainly was the neatest and tidiest ward in the whole hospital, and, also, one of the quietest.

However, as I mentioned previously, Mum fondly remembers Staff Nurse Mackenzie before she became Sister Luney, as the kindest and most gentle nurse on the ward; she treated Grannie with great care and empathy, so who am I to criticise her ward management methods?

First-year nurses did a lot of cleaning, but more so in ward five. We would scrub the drip stands with brillo pads, and make sure all the bed wheels faced the same direction. The bed screens were always pulled back neatly and evenly, and the patient lockers were never out of place or untidy.

The disinfectants we used were very strong and wouldn't be allowed now with control of substances hazardous to health regulations, otherwise known as COSHH, I was often accused by my brothers of smelling like a hospital when we were eating our evening meal round the kitchen table at home, especially during my stint in theatre.

My favourite wards were ward six, male orthopaedic, and ward four, female orthopaedic. Mr. Simpson and Mr. McArdle were the orthopaedic consultants. Ward six was my very first ward as a fresh out of college and wet behind the ear's student nurse. It was also the first ward I worked in after I qualified as a staff nurse.

Part of a new patient's initiation on ward six revolved around his first request for a bed pan.

The screens were pulled around the bed, and the often-cold stainless-steel bed pan, although, we were supposed to run it under the hot tap before dispensing it, was placed under the patient and we left them to their business and ablutions.

At the same time, some other patients, who were bored having been bedbound for weeks on traction, would switch off their radios and a request for everyone to 'shush' went around the ward. This was usually followed by the poor unsuspecting patient being bombarded with toilet rolls flying over the top of the screens from all directions.

Once bitten, twice shy as the saying goes… constipation often ensued. We used quite a lot of laxatives on that ward.

I remember one afternoon when I was in my second year, I was put into a bath of cold water in the patients' bathroom in ward four. My colleagues kindly removed my shoes and cap first. When I eventually got out, I discovered, although, was not surprised to find, a layer of KY jelly inside my shoes, The reason for this? It was my last day on that ward, and I assume it was quiet at the time. No other reason required! The patients loved it. I got a round of applause when I emerged, dripping from head to foot, squelching in my shoes. It was all done in good spirits, and, only to those who could take it as the joke it was meant to be, I suspect. I wonder if anything similar ever happened to Nurse Mackenzie?

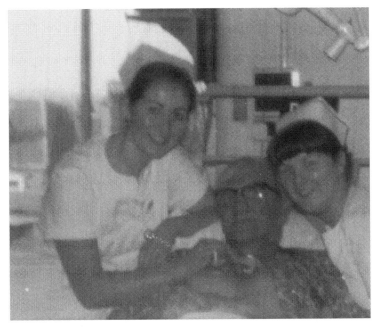

Figure 12 *That's me on the left on ward three, KI, with Evelyn Lynch and a very sweet patient!*

Every day we carried out four-hourly temperature, pulse and respirations on all patients, more commonly known as four-hourly TPRs, plus four-hourly back rounds. A back round involved going around the ward with the back trolley which was a cumbersome stainless-steel contraption which had a sink and huge stainless-steel jugs into which we poured warm water. It housed sheets, pillowcases, draw sheets, incontinence pads, nightwear etc. – everything required to wash a non-ambulant patient and make them comfortable. There was also a selection of lotions and potions, but after the first round of the morning, mainly spirit and talc was used. We would rub spirit onto the main pressure areas – heels, sacral area (buttocks) elbows etc., and then a sprinkling of talcum powder.

Occasionally, a patient was admitted to the hospital with pressure sores. I have seen a cavity that was big enough for a fist to fit inside, bone clearly exposed. They were excruciatingly painful and unpleasant for the patients and were to be avoided at all costs, and finding that a patient developed a pressure sore whilst in our care was cause for disappointment, even shame among staff. Moving and turning immobile patients was essential to relieve pressure. In the late 70s we used egg white and oxygen. Egg whites were whisked up in a disposable foil dish with a fork and applied to the pressure sore and then dried with oxygen from a cylinder using a rubber tube. Did it work better than other methods? Who knows? But it was popular at the time.

After the back round was completed, we returned to the sluice, disposed of the soiled linen and emptied the dirty water out of the large stainless-steel bucket which was situated underneath the sink. We then scrubbed the trolley with Glitto scouring powder, the hospital version of Ajax or Vim which were commonly used at that time in households to clean sinks and baths, rinsed it, and then polished it with surgical spirits until it shone. It was then re-stocked ready for the next round.

I, like many of my colleagues, took great pride in this procedure and loved to see the massive steel trolley gleaming and covered with a crisp, clean white draw sheet.

Patients' bowel habits took up a lot of attention. Sad but true. It appeared that both patients and nurses were obsessed by the frequency of bowel movements, but a bit like the chicken and the egg, I am unsure as to which came first. I am being flippant, but actually, monitoring a patient's bowel movements is important, especially post-operatively and in the elderly.

Every morning, during the TPR round, all patients on the ward were asked if their bowels had moved that day. If they had failed to produce a stool, it was noted on the observation chart hanging on the end of the bed and was worthy of a mention in afternoon report given to the late-duty staff. If this wasn't a first offense, the patient was given a dose of 'yellow peril'. Unfortunately I can't remember what its proper name was, suffice to say it was a gentle laxative and was on almost every prescription chart.

Occasionally we would admit a patient with acute or chronic constipation. Usually an elderly, malnourished and dehydrated soul complaining of abdominal pain and loss of appetite. Severe constipation can and does cause great discomfort. It can also make a patient feel very unwell, hence nurse's preoccupation with prevention.

The first line of attack, after all oral purgatives had been tried, and subsequently failed, were various types of suppositories. If suppositories didn't work a disposable enema would be prescribed. And, finally, if we were satisfied that all else had failed, we would be instructed to administer a soap and water enema, and/or a manual bowel evacuation, which is as unpleasant for all concerned as it sounds, but most especially for the poor patient.

A soap and water enema was a sight to behold. It always reminded me of pictures I had seen of the suffragettes being force fed, although, obviously, we used an altogether different part of the anatomy. Firstly, we collected a brown glass bottle of enema soap from pharmacy. The contents were mixed in a jug with tepid water. The patient was made as comfortable as possible and reassured. Then they were asked to lie on their side, and an ample supply of incontinence pads was placed underneath their nether regions, making sure dignity was always preserved. Two nurses were required for this procedure. A soft, orange, rubber tube was inserted into the rectum and held in place by one of the nurses.

The nurse in charge of pouring the enema soap into the funnel, which was attached to one end of the tube, made sure there was a kink in the tube before pouring the soapy fluid into the funnel. Then the fluid was slowly released into the tube and consequently the patient. This was often as messy and unpleasant as you might be imagining. If it produced a result (and it usually did), the patient's obvious relief and gratitude made it very satisfying indeed. One time, when I oversaw the funnel and jug, a colleague popped her head around the bedside curtain to ask a question, when I turned to reply, the full funnel tipped over, spilling the contents into the cap of my able assistant. It was very hard not to laugh as watery enema soap silently dribbled down her face.

Occasionally, we had to perform a manual evacuation of some poor unfortunate patient's bowel.

I distinctly remember performing this procedure when I was on night duty. It was Hogmanay (New Year's Eve). The town stretched out beneath the ward window, Christmas lights were visible, and the streets were crowded with revellers waiting for the all-important midnight bell chimes welcoming in a brand-new year. I suspect many of the celebrators found their way to Casualty a few hours later, but again, I digress.

It was necessary to perform a manual evacuation on a poor little lady who was in great discomfort having been constipated for quite some time. Donning two pairs of surgical gloves, and an apron, I softly explained to the lady what I was about to do and to reassure her as much as I could. I started to manually remove the impacted, hard faeces from her rectum. Unbelievably, she barely seemed to notice what was happening; she had been in pain for some time and was from the generation of people who do not like to make a fuss. I heard the bells chime in the church next door. It was twelve o'clock, the birth of a new year. I could hear faint and distant cheers of 'Happy New Year' coming up from the streets below. I had neither the heart, nor the inclination to wish my patient a Happy New Year.

CHAPTER 6

LESSONS IN LIFE

"If a patient is cold, if a patient is feverish, if a patient is faint, if he is sick after taking food, if he has a bed sore, it is generally the fault not of the disease but of the nursing."

- Florence Nightingale

Student and pupil nurses were assessed by the ward sister or staff nurse at the end of a stint, known as a block, on a ward. My first report was completed by Sister Biggar in ward six.

It was an excellent first report, but in a comments section at the end of the form she wrote: *'Nurse Heron tends to be rather over emotional'.*

This observation by Sister Biggar had been made after an incident involving a lovely white-haired old gentleman. He was admitted to ward six after being brutally beaten up and burgled in his own home. I was genuinely horrified; this was the kind of thing I had only read about in the newspapers or seen on the news, but here I was, aged eighteen, face to face with a real-life victim. The poor old soul was badly shaken up both mentally and physically. He was so gentle, and thankful for everything that was done for him by any member of staff. He needed an x-ray, and as per procedure, I as the junior nurse was told to accompany him to the radiology department and assist where necessary. When the porter arrived with the large, brown, leather wheelchair, Mr. X got flustered, and before I could stop him, he sat on the rather substantial foot rest instead of the actual chair.

As I have said, ward six, being an orthopaedic ward had more than its fair share of young men who had been involved in motorbike accidents or car accidents, which often resulted in months of bed rest and the young patients getting very bored. Patients tended to watch any activity in the ward with great curiosity and when my lovely patient sat on the foot rest, a few of the patients pointed at him and roared with laughter. I felt so upset by their thoughtlessness and seeming unkindness.

While Mr. X was waiting for his x-ray, he told me what had happened to him and how frightened he had been. The low-lives had stolen money and personal items from him after they had beaten him up in his own home and left him battered, bruised, cut and very shaken. They robbed him of his dignity and peace of mind as well as his personal belongings. Totally unforgivable. I got my delightful and fragile patient safely and comfortably back to bed after his x-ray, and then promptly went into the sluice and burst into tears. I was crying for my patient, I was crying about the injustice, I was crying because some of the other patients had seemed to be cruel and uncaring.

That was where Sister Biggar found me, sobbing into a paper towel.

She was very sympathetic, and said it showed that I cared. She then went on to explain that I would see and hear of many things which would and could be much worse. She told me that although a nurse must be compassionate, he or she must also learn how to become emotionally detached and carry out their duties to the very best of their ability without ever betraying how upset they may be feeling. Not only for their sake, but much more importantly for the sake of the patient.

I will never forget that conversation.

When I got home, I tried to tell Mum and Dad about it, what she had said, but couldn't without welling up again. The look on dad's face said it all.

'I knew it, I knew you would be like this. Is this how it will be for the next three years?' He wasn't unsympathetic, just worried that I would not be able to handle what would be thrown at me during my training.

I must say that sometimes emotions swung the other way, and nurses could find themselves laughing quietly and quite inappropriately at times. This is difficult to explain without making nurses sound as thoughtless and unkind as I had thought the patients who laughed at Mr. X had been. It was always short-lived, and hopefully well disguised, a mixture of nerves and a coping mechanism.

Casualty, or Accident and Emergency as it is now known, was very different to life on the wards and could be quite terrifying for a student nurse. There seemed to be a never-ending stream of fractures, dislocations, burns, eye injuries, soft tissue injuries; many were alcohol related, especially on night duty, and of course there were the well-known regulars who were after medication or a warm place to sleep for the night.

I enjoyed working in Casualty. It was varied, and there were often some unusual sights and surprises. Many of which were quite an eye-opener for an eighteen-year-old.

I witnessed a wide assortment of items, ranging from a Coleman's mustard jar filled with ball bearings, a Mr. Matey bubble bath bottle, to a curved gents' umbrella handle, stuck in various orifices.

One extremely busy Saturday afternoon Kilmarnock football team was playing at home which always made for an eventful and action-packed shift. The waiting room was heaving, a cacophony of moans, groans and complaints. It was literally standing room only. I went out to call for the next patient. After I called his name, a man stood up, he was wearing a white top, white trousers, and a rather dirty-looking, blood-stained, navy-blue stiped apron. He was a butcher who had come a cropper.

Holding his injured hand aloft, he followed me through to the treatment room where there was another small waiting area which was crowded with patients at various stages of treatment and procedures. My patient had sliced the top off a finger, and although it had obviously been bleeding copiously, the now congealed blood was well contained in what looked like a neat white cloth which in turn was enclosed in a very effective, flexible covering.

I explained that he would not have long to wait until he was seen, and that I would leave his dressing intact until I could get him into a treatment room.

'Your dressing looks very robust,' I congratulated him on his choice of covering, genuinely impressed by his efforts to dress his wound. 'Where did you get it from?'

'Out of a packet of three from the machine in the gents',' came the sniggered reply. My cheeks flushed bright red, I and scuttled away as fast as my legs could carry me, with the sound of not so muffled laughter ringing in my ears.

Night duty was always eventful in Casualty. For one thing, several nurses on duty in the wards would come to the department and have their dinner break there. The wards, as you might imagine, were dimly lit and mostly quiet, so going to the bustling, well-lit Casualty department meant you could almost forget that it was the middle of the night.

One alternative to having a dinner break in Casualty, was to have forty winks in the ward linen cupboard. Strictly against the rules, but oh so welcome some nights. The shelves were wooden and slatted and the perfect size to lie down on. The cupboard was always warm and inviting, especially if you hadn't managed to sleep during the day. I tried it a few times, but nearly got caught by the night nursing officcr when he walked in one night. I think he chose not to see me. That said, I found it far too easy to fall asleep and way too hard to wake up again after the thirty-minute break, so Casualty was by far the best option for me.

One night an elderly couple were pronounced dead on arrival in Casualty (DOA). They had been involved in a road traffic accident with a drunk driver. The drunk driver, who had also been brought to the hospital with minor injuries, was unaware of this fact. He was in a treatment room cracking jokes and complaining about his cuts, bruises, and pain. That is when the advice given to me by Sister Biggar during my appraisal really hit home. Repeat after me, 'remain emotionally detached'.

Another difficult night involved a young man who was only a couple of years older than me. I recognised his name although I didn't really know him. He had taken a massive overdose. We got many cries for help, but this boy really meant it. It was my first close-up, real-life crash call. The crash team, which consisted of designated bleep holders, a mixture of medical and nursing staff, came thundering into the department minutes after the call went out advising them of cardiac arrest in Casualty. I was too shocked and inexperienced to be of any real help. I felt overwhelmed and underqualified. That said, I followed instructions to the best of my ability although part of me really wanted to run away and hide until it was all over. Doctors and senior members of staff were barking out commands, monitors bleeped, intravenous fluids were flowing, adrenaline, atropine, lignocaine and soda bic. (sodium bicarbonate) were requested. The defibrillator was useless. The patient was in asystole and there was nothing more that could be done to save him. My first experience of real-life cardiac arrest and cardiopulmonary resuscitation had been a baptism of fire, shocking and emotional. Thankfully and frankly it was never as frightening again. It is astonishing what you can become used to given time and experience.

Another drug overdose sticks in my mind. A young girl came in one evening, and after careful questioning it was established by the junior doctor, who had been working for about seventy-two hours, what she had taken, when and why. She was in no immediate danger, at least not from the drugs she had taken.

'Were you trying to kill yourself?' asked the doctor a touch too sympathetically.

'Yes, I had an argument with my dad about my boyfriend,' came the sobbing emotional reply.

The doctor calmly looked at his wrist watch, gazed into the girl's eyes and said, 'You could still manage it. There is plenty of time for the pills to take effect.'

Her howls of misery could be heard in the waiting room. It may sound very harsh and unethical by today's standards, but I am willing to bet she didn't ever try it again.

Miss Cairns, the Senior Nursing Officer, was very kind to me, as was Miss Harris who had seemingly terrorised me in the past, when I sustained a back injury which plagues me to this day. I must point out, that having become a manager, and experienced misunderstanding and even hostility from some members of my staff, I now realise what a difficult job they were doing. Oh, the beauty of hindsight.

My back injury was sustained after a rather rotund patient had slipped down her bed, and was unable to pull herself back up again. It was usual practice at that time for two nurses to use one of the several lifting techniques we had been taught in class to manoeuvre a patient back into a sitting position in bed. But, occasionally we needed to put our knees on the bed, shoulders under the patient's armpits to move the patient successfully.

Almost immediately after we had lifted the patient, I felt intense pain. I actually looked over my shoulder, because it felt like I had been whacked with a heavy object across my lower back.

I can still remember the deep embarrassment of lying on a trolley in the corridor outside x-ray wearing a hospital gown. My cap and uniform were on the shelf underneath me. I could hear outpatients whispering, 'I think that is a nurse on that trolley,' with obvious interest and curiosity. I pretended to be asleep and hoped I would be taken for my x-ray sooner rather than later. Although it is almost forty years since that incident, I am still suffering the consequences today. My back has been the cause of debilitation and excruciating pain over the years and I would not wish it on my worst enemy.

The consultant's ward round was conducted with utmost reverence, verging on hero worship. Everything in the ward was washed, polished, put in its place (that included the patients) and a hushed atmosphere was the order of the day. Even if a patient coughed he or she would get a frosty look from Sister. Okay, slight exaggeration there, but hopefully you get the picture.

Once, during a ward round a patient asked me for a urine bottle. He needed to pass urine, and he needed to do it right away. He claimed he could not and would not wait until the ward round was over, and rightly so.

I pulled the screens around his bed and got him a bottle. Urine bottles were made of glass at that time and were quite heavy. Because of his hydrocele, a sac filled with fluid which forms around the testicle, passing urine straight into a bottle was not as easy as it may sound, and he required a bit of assistance. I tried my best to assist him, but urine started spilling over the top of the bottle and onto the floor. I specifically remember I was wearing my lovely, brand-new, white shoes with hundreds of tiny pin holes in them, bought for me in Canada by my grandparents. No one else had a pair like them. Inevitably my feet were covered in urine too, not to mention my hands, making them slippery, and the bottle dropped to the floor with a loud clunk, not once, but several times. Fortunately, the patient found it rather amusing, so I did what I usually do in circumstances like this and promptly had a fit of the giggles and was made worse when Sister's frilly-hat-topped head popped around the screen. Her fuming red face demanding an end to the melee, and an explanation after the ward round.

Getting false teeth mixed up is a bit of an urban myth, but I swear I did this.

I hated night duty with a passion. It seemed so unnatural and I found it hard to sleep during the day. If the ward was quiet, which was unusual to be fair, I struggled to keep my eyes open when it got to about three in the morning.

I was assigned to the denture round. This involved collecting patient's dentures from the top of their lockers. Denture-wearing patients were provided with denture cups if they didn't have one of their own. These were made of plastic and had a space to write the patient's name on the lid, which we rarely did because they were forever being replaced. It was fairly time consuming – collect the dentures, go to the sluice, brush the dentures with toothpaste, rinse, place into a new receptacle if required, and then return them to the locker ready for breakfast in the morning. Kilmarnock Infirmary having Nightingale-type wards, long, with deep bay windows, meant there was a lot of walking involved.

In my tired warped wisdom, I came up with a plan. If I collected them all together, kept them in order and returned them in reverse order it would save a lot of time and effort. When I had a stack of sparkling white dentures which had been cleaned in record time I felt very pleased with myself. I set off placing the pots carefully in reverse order as planned, beside each bed.

I got to a patient that I knew for definite had dentures. Goodness knows, I had fished said dentures out of a bowl of porridge often enough. I had even cleaned off what I thought was black pudding, only to discover that the patient was on iron supplements which had made their faeces black. Yes, there was no doubt at all, this patient definitely wore dentures, but I had a big problem. I had run out. There were no more containers left on my trolley.

What on earth had gone wrong?

It my jaded confusion, I had failed to note which patients did not wear dentures, and therefore I had placed a denture pot on the locker of non-denture wearers. It was a bit of a confused mess to say the least, but with some help, I managed to get it sorted out. It took a lot of time and effort. Lesson learned.

Another night duty, another ward, found me having another of my fits of nervous giggles. I went into the duty room to answer the telephone. The phone ringing at that time of the morning could only mean one thing. An admission.

I was told to expect an elderly lady with a fractured femur. The cot ward was full; one lady was getting well enough to merit transfer into the main ward. As luck would have it, there was an empty bed in the main ward, so it would be a simple case of swapping the beds around.

I approached the slumbering lady. She looked so peaceful and comfortable, her snowy white hair strewn across her pillow. Giving her a gentle nudge, and saying her name, I quietly explained what we were about to do. She opened her eyes a shade and nodded, and then promptly closed them again, the pink frill on the neck of her nightie ruffled around her chin making her look rather angelic.

My colleague and I set to work. The main body of the ward had a long table in the middle of the floor, above which, was suspended a pendant light with an aluminium shade. The lamp almost reached the table top and was primarily used on night duty to allow just enough illumination to allow nurses to study or write reports. We moved the table to one side of the ward, and then manoeuvred the empty bed down into the cot ward, parking it in the corridor just inside the double, swinging doors.

'We will move you now Mrs. Y, it won't take long, just stay nice and still,' we reassuringly informed our patient.

In our haste to complete this midnight flitting, we forgot about the lamp, which, minus the table was about chest height, perfect to contact the metal bedhead as we pushed into it. There was a loud clang as metal touched metal causing quite a few of the patients in the ward to stir and mutter about the commotion. Mrs. Y, by this time was sitting bolt upright in bed, just in time to see the pendulous lamp shade miss her nose by inches as it bounced off the bed and swung round again, giving her quite a shock. I think it gave me and my colleague much more of a shock. Yet another valuable lesson learned.

No damage was done; we offered Mrs. Y a nice cup of tea and a slice of hot buttered toast, and fetched tea for the other, normally audibly challenged patients who were within earshot and didn't want to miss out on the midnight feast.

The same near-miss happening today would involve an incident report being filed on paper and on the intranet, to be reviewed at various organisational levels including Health and Safety representatives, Human Resources and Senior Management. It would be on the agenda at the weekly and monthly Heads of Department meetings for weeks and months on end until a satisfactory resolution was found to prevent such an incident happening again, and culprits dealt with to the satisfaction of all involved. All files being kept for a statutory amount of time. That's what is known as progress.

I may sound facetious. I do recognise that, in oh so many ways, times have changed for the better, for patients and staff wellbeing and safety, but sometimes a little common sense can go a very long way.

Whilst on the subject of mishaps I will take this opportunity to apologise to the patients in ward six who lost about fifteen minutes of their precious visiting time because of me, in the summer of 1981.

Visiting hour was strictly adhered to. One hour long, two visitors to a bed. It was the highlight of the day for most patients. For ward staff, it meant making sure everything was ship shape and Bristol fashion. Lockers were tidied, beds straightened, everything organised and, in its place, presenting a picture-perfect ward to the forthcoming members of the public. Nursing staff used the time to study in between finding vases for the inevitable bunches of flowers, or gratefully accepting the odd box of chocolates.

Patient meals were wheeled up to the wards in large, heated cabinets. The nurse in charge would make sure the plates were suitably warm and would often decide what patients would eat and how much. Presentation was key, for instance, elderly people do not like having too much food on their plates and the nurse in charge could supplement the meal as she saw fit to benefit the patient's recovery.

Sister or staff nurse would serve up each individual meal and the rest of the staff would stand in front of the trolley and wait to take the plates and hand them out to the correct patient. Some patients would get up and eat at the table, but many, especially on orthopaedic wards were unable to do so, and would eat in bed. Junior nurses were often asked to help any patient who required help or coaxing. After meal time, we had to gather in all the dirty plates, dishes and cutlery.

Used cutlery was placed into a washing up bowl filled with hot soapy water, uneaten food was scraped into a large slop bucket. There was an open, two-tiered trolley for this purpose.

That evening, the meal had been sent up late, so we were working against the clock to get everything cleared away before visiting hour began. For dessert, the patients had been offered stewed apples with either custard or ice cream. Many of the young lads had both. (Ice cream and custard was a night duty favourite with nurses, as were chips and coleslaw. Always available and reliable in the middle of the night.) I hurriedly put the empty, and some not so empty, bowls onto the lower shelf of the trolley having decided that it would be quicker to do this and scrape them clean when we returned to the ward kitchen. In my haste, one rather full bowl shot off the back of the trolley and went spinning down the shiny polished ward floor spraying custard hither and thither. Who knew a small bowl could contain so much custard? The bright yellow sauce was all over the floor. There was much merriment, hilarity, and even some applause, and of course a floor to clean before the doors could be opened to the patiently waiting visitors with their flowers, bottles of Lucozade and boxes of chocolates.

Sister Marjory Kerr, treasurer of the staff social committee at Ayrshire Central Hospital, Irvine, hands over a cheque for £2,000 to Mrs Margaret Bicker, senior midwifery tutor of Ayrshire and Arran Health Board. The money will be spend for the benefit of the patients at Ayrshire Central Hospital.

Figure 13: *Me in front row, far left.*
Photograph courtesy of Kilmarnock Standard

CHAPTER 7

THEATRE

"A surgeon is surrounded by people who are sick, discouraged, afraid, embittered, dying – but also courageous, loving, wise, compassionate and alive."

- Bernie Siegel

I did not enjoy my stint in theatre. I much preferred it when patients were awake and responsive.

In my opinion, in the 1970s, it seemed that student nurses were only tolerated in theatre because they absolutely had to be. Generally, it was best to be seen and not heard.

I felt that the theatre suite was an outlandish place. Different rules and regulations, an even stricter hierarchy than on the wards, and, sometimes, extremely temperamental surgeons (some things never change… you know who you are). Also, my stint was in the winter, so it was dark when I arrived at work, I spent all day in the theatre suite which offered next to no natural light, and it was dark when I went home again.

It did not bode well for me that I thought there were building and joinery repairs being carried out the first time I heard an orthopaedic list being executed. Suffice to say there was quite a bit of hammering, sawing and drilling going on which had nothing to do with the building, and leave it there.

Doctor McNab was an anaesthetist who had the reputation of putting student nurses on the spot with his mini tutorials and expectations. During our time in theatre, we student nurses were expected to spend at least one day with an anaesthetist, and I prayed I would not be allocated to Doctor McNab, but, yes, you've guessed it, I was.

'Ask loads of questions, he loves that,' I was told authoritatively by a nurse who was in the year above me.

Doctor McNab was very old school. He always wore a bow tie and loved nothing better than to reminisce about his days as a junior doctor, all the scrapes he got into, and the beautiful young ladies he took to dances and grand balls. I found him quite fascinating and rather sweet as well as intimidating at times.

I had been asked to shadow him for the day, and as the afternoon approached, I felt my day with him had gone quite well. I did learn a lot from the great man. The last case of the day was upon us before I knew it, and I began to relax a little, feeling that I had managed to build up a rapport with Doctor M. Later, in my theatre stint, I found out why certain cases were left to last. At that time, however, I was in blissful ignorance.

The last patient on the theatre list was duly anaesthetised, lying seemingly lifeless and swathed in theatre greens on the operating table.

I was feeling a little bit tired by then; it had been an emotionally charged day for me and I was relieved to have survived a day with Dr McNab. I wracked my brains to think of a suitable question I could ask to reassure Doctor M. that I was still as keen as mustard. The patient was having a leg amputated and the very thought of this made me shudder. Very few things in my nursing career have phased me, amputations being one of them.

'Why is the leg being amputated, Doctor McNab?' I questioned in a hushed, rather intimate, and by now familiar, tone.

'I beg your pardon? I think you should tell ME why this poor unfortunate soul is having his leg cut off,' he boomed rather overdramatically and effectively causing almost everyone in theatre to look in our direction.

'Have you no sense of smell, girl?' he continued.

By this time, the surgeon had removed the malodourous,

gangrenous limb, and it was being taken unceremoniously to the sluice by the theatre porter to be bagged up and sent for incineration. The surgeon was expertly forming a flap consisting of preserved fascia, muscle and skin over the now exposed bone to create a neat stump.

'Go into the sluice, and examine the leg, Nurse, and then report back to me.'

Off I went, trembling with apprehension and embarrassment.

The theatre porter was very kind and did not remove the leg from its plastic bag casing. He merely asked me to wait a few minutes, and told me what to say to Doctor McNab, who could be easily appeased once he had generated a bit of drama for everyone.

Once the patient had been taken to recovery, it was a case of all hands on deck as the theatre was decontaminated, and literally scrubbed from top to bottom with exceptionally strong disinfectant before it could be deemed safe to use again. Ceiling, walls, floor, the lot were rubbed clean.

To earn extra brownie points from the theatre staff, I opted to be added to the 'on call' rota.

I had been reliably informed by one of the staff nurses who was quite approachable, that being on call was the very best way to learn about theatre and its goings on. With less staff around than during the day, you were more likely to become involved with the case in hand and not just stand by and watch or count swabs. The main thing was to make sure you knew exactly where everything was kept, and the correct names for instruments etc. Surgeons are notoriously temperamental and apt to throw the odd temper tantrum and did not suffer students gladly.

One snowy December night as I lay fast asleep in my cosy bed, the telephone rang. We had one phone in our house, it sat on a kidney-shaped table, which had been made by my dad, and was situated at the bottom of the stairway. It was mustard coloured and had a large dial which made a satisfying burring noise when you dialled a number. It also had a very loud ring.

I rushed downstairs to answer it before it woke the whole household.

'Nurse Heron, you are needed in theatre as soon as possible.' I felt so important, it was like something I had seen in a film once, then reality kicked in. I got dressed quickly and ran across the dimly lit road to Gran and Papa's garage. The snowflakes looked pretty as they fell beneath the street lamps. I had the foresight to ask Gran and Papa for the keys earlier that day, just in case I was called out. I managed to start the mini clubman without overdoing the choke and set off for Kilmarnock.

Before I even got to the hospital I was quaking with nerves. I had only just passed my driving test the month before and was an anxious driver who had mostly driven in daylight, also this was my first time driving in snow. Hill starts were not my strong point, and I will give you a little clue, the Casualty entrance to the hospital was on Hill Street.

It was such a strange drive into Kilmarnock. It was so quiet, not a soul to be seen. I felt as if I was in some sort of weird snow globe. The snow was lying quite thickly on the roads and pavements. I parked in St Joseph's Church car park which, needless to say, was empty.

When I arrived in theatre, about two in the morning, it was eerily quiet. I was first to arrive in my enthusiasm and anxiety.

I got changed, and by the time I had my hair piled up inside my cap Sister had arrived, one of the nice ones thankfully; she seemed remarkably and unusually chatty and put me at my ease, until she informed me that the case we were expecting was a boating accident. The patient involved had had his foot partially severed and would require an amputation. My heart flipped and sank... not another one.

The operation went without a hitch, until the surgeon, failing to locate the stainless-steel run -around (basically a basin on wheels), threw the foot, or rather what was left of it, at me in a temper, shouting, 'Get rid of this.'

Now, it is worth mentioning, many of my fellow students were not called out at all, they got the glory of volunteering, but none of the aggravation.

I was called out twice.

The second call out was to a suspected appendicitis.

I wasn't first to arrive this time, but quickly set to work setting up as best as I could, following precise instructions from Sister.

The appendicectomy went without a hitch. I thought the patient looked slightly familiar, but up until the point he was being returned to male surgical, I didn't have much time to think about it.

Imagine my surprise when I looked at the patient notes afterwards and discovered it was the son of Mum and Dad's best friends. We still joke that I have seen parts of him that no one else in his family have ever seen.

CHAPTER 8

THE MIDWIFERY YEARS 1981-1986

"Whoever heard of a midwife as a literary heroine? Yet midwifery is the very stuff of drama. Every child is conceived either in love or lust, is born in pain, followed by joy or sometimes remorse. A midwife is in the thick of it, she sees it all."

- Jennifer Worth

Our class, which had started general training in February 1978, was the first class to sit State final exams in the new College of Nursing located in the grounds of North Ayrshire District General Hospital (NADGH), a brand-new building which was going to replace Kilmarnock Infirmary which was really beginning to show its age. Thankfully, the name was changed, and it is now known as University Hospital Crosshouse.

I have to say, I absolutely loved KI and the new hospital with its six bedded wards and single rooms did nothing for me. I knew it was necessary to replace the old infirmary, but NADGH lacked character and soul, and let's face it, it didn't exactly trip off the tongue. When it was first built it had a flat roof and I thought it looked like a huge white box of a building.

I nearly missed out on sitting state finals because my back problem had chosen to play up big time. To this day my back can go into spasm when I am anxious. I remember Miss Cairns announcing to me, quite matter-of-factly, that I would not be joining the rest of my class when we took our exams, as I clutched onto a grey filing cabinet for support whilst handing her my sick note. But resolutely, I did. And now it was time to find out what the result of three years' hard slog and studying would be. Each candidate was informed of their pass or fail status by post.

My mum was working in a gents' clothes shop in Kilmarnock at that time, but I begged her to wait until the first post had been delivered. Yes, we had two postal deliveries in those days, imagine!

I called her from the public call box in casualty reception.

'No post yet, and I will need to leave very soon,' came the reply to my apprehensive question.

Returning to the ward, I was beside myself with nerves and anticipation. I was on early duty and was less than useless to my colleagues that morning. I asked permission to go and make another phone call. Sister nodded sympathetically and actually allowed me to use the phone in the duty room.

Mum answered quickly. 'I have an envelope addressed to you,' said Mum. 'Shall I open it?' she asked evenly.

What was wrong with this woman? Of course I wanted her to open it.

'It says you have passed,' said Mum, steadily.

I can't honestly remember what happened after that, other than returning to the ward and being congratulated. I had done it. I was now Staff Nurse Heron, and it felt fantastic.

Dad would often pick me up after work to drive me home. That day, he was standing in the corridor outside casualty waiting for me and I just couldn't help it, I burst into tears of relief and joy. We were not an emotionally demonstrative family, so that was a very big deal indeed.

To know I had made my parents proud was the proverbial icing on the cake.

*

I decided to start my midwifery training after a short spell as a staff nurse on ward six. It seemed to be a good idea to get the qualification under my belt, especially if I wanted to venture into District Nursing or Health Visiting, which I really wanted to do. Not least because I would not be expected to work nights.

Midwifery training took place at Ayrshire and Arran College of Nursing in Irvine just as the general training had, but the classrooms were in the main maternity hospital, and not in the administrative buildings. Because of this, we were required to wear full uniform at all times, even when sitting in class all day.

I was in the last group of student midwives to be offered the year-long course; it was increased to a year and a half, and rightly so in my humble opinion. You could not train to become a midwife without first completing the three-year Registered General Nurse course.

It was case of hitting the ground running. I was the lowest of the low again, and the workload both in and out of the classroom was intense. We spent every Monday in class, even when we had ward placements.

I was pleasantly surprised to discover that I excelled at midwifery. Well, the theory at least.

I found midwifery to be fascinating, and rarely found myself with marks less than 90% for course work and exams.

The exception to this was oral exams, where we were given props such as forceps, or an obstetric doll and pelvis, and asked for accurate, detailed demonstrations and knowledgeable banter.

We were required to palpate a 'real' patient, answer all sorts of gruelling questions about period of gestation, fundal height, lie of the foetus and of course, perform successful auscultation of the foetal heart (listening to the baby's heart beat).

Often, miscellaneous questions would be thrown at us.

'Define haemolytic disease of the newborn.'

'Define haemorrhagic disease of the newborn.'

'Define transverse arrest, involution of the uterus, transverse lie, inversion of the uterus...'

It was all extremely nerve wracking... Well, to me at least.

I found the subject of twins to be rather confusing. My fellow student midwives found this hilarious because I was engaged to be married to a monozygotic twin (uniovular or identical) as opposed to a dizygotic or binovular twin (see what I mean?) And they mistakenly reckoned this would make me an expert on the subject.

Our wedding was planned for June 1982, so it was rather a full-on year one way or another.

Before qualifying, each student midwife had to deliver forty babies. This would often involve staying behind after a shift ended if you knew a lady was about to go into the second stage of labour.

When I was assigned to Kilmarnock Maternity Home for a short spell, I was determined to deliver a baby there, because that was where I was born. I am delighted to say that I did.

We carried our log books with us always, and when we had delivered a baby, the midwife who conducted it would sign it off for us. In the early days, it was so difficult to imagine the book ever being filled, but it was surprising just how quickly it was.

One particular night duty I shall never forget, I was the only student on duty, and the labour suite was in full swing. I was literally running from one delivery to another.

We would get scrubbed up, don a gown, mask and gloves and follow instructions given to us by a qualified midwife.

It is vitally important for a midwife to understand the relationship of the foetus to the uterus and pelvis. This relationship determines which part of the foetus will enter the pelvic brim first. Without boring you with the technicalities, this determines how the delivery is conducted; a vertex presentation, spontaneous vertex delivery (SVD) is most common in about 96.8% of deliveries. This offers the smallest diameter. Other presentations have much bigger diameters which can potentially cause injury to the mother during delivery.

That evening we had missed the fact that the foetus was not in flexion. Flexion means that a compact, ovoid mass forms, with the smallest possible head circumference for delivery. Any deviation from this could spell trouble.

Put simply, a well tucked-in head will be smaller in circumference and therefore less likely to case complications or injury.

What we had was an undiagnosed face to pubes and therefore a large head circumference, which meant that a third-degree tear was a distinct possibility if not conducted correctly.

A third-degree tear is, thankfully, rare. It causes post-partum complications because the anal sphincter and sometimes even the rectum is torn. Usually, an episiotomy (an incision made into the perineum to enlarge the vaginal orifice) will be performed to prevent it.

The mum was a very petite lady, and she had a very big bump. She was getting extremely tired, and the foetus began to show signs of distress. The foetal heart rate dropped, and we noticed some fresh meconium (baby's first stool) staining in the amniotic fluid, a clear sign that the baby has poor muscle tone due to lack of oxygen.

Suddenly and without warning, mum gave an almighty push and a very floppy, blue-tinged baby shot out. After the cord was clamped and cut and, his airway was cleared he was unresponsive to certain stimuli. His Apgar score was recorded at one minute and five minutes post-delivery. Apgar is the measure of a newborn's physical condition, either two, one or no points being allocated for heart rate, respiratory effort, muscle tone, response to stimulations and skin colouration. He was taken swiftly to the special care baby unit (SCBU) which was across the hall from the labour suite.

Sister and I stayed with Mum and waited for the third stage of labour (delivery of the placenta).

Mum had most definitely sustained a third-degree tear and would require careful suturing by an obstetrician. Midwives at that time only sutured episiotomy scars which were straightforward and uncomplicated.

Everything was done to reassure the new mum, and we had received news from SCBU that baby was improving and doing just fine.

I went to the sluice to inspect the placenta; management of the third stage of labour is not complete until the placenta has been thoroughly checked to make sure that it is intact and that the membranes are complete. Any products of delivery left in the uterus may prevent effective uterine contraction, allowing vessels to bleed freely which can cause post-partum haemorrhage. As I carried out this procedure, I found I could barely see. Tears were pouring down my face, making my now under-the-chin mask damp and soggy.

I felt so inadequate, I had been convinced that the baby would not survive. I felt vexed that the unfortunate new mum would need to take laxatives for weeks. I decided there and then that I did not want to deliver another baby. Ever!

Sister came to find me and was very supportive. She assured me that I was not to blame.

'You thought the baby was dead, didn't you?' Sister asked me gently. I couldn't answer. Hot, salty tears now cascaded down my face and I was sobbing.

She took me to the SCBU to see the nine-pound-plus little bundle of joy, now nicely pink and sleeping soundly, oblivious to the hullabaloo his entrance into the world had caused. Sister said she was glad I was having a good cry.

'It shows you care. This is not a reason to give up, you can give up when you stop caring about your patients.'

Sound advice indeed. It was my last night duty for a while, and I couldn't wait to get home, have a good cry and hopefully sleep.

*

Part of our midwifery training involved work out in the community. I loved it. It was so varied and interesting, plus, we got to wear our uniforms to and from work, unheard of for ward nurses.

As I mentioned earlier, a small part of my community placement was spent in Kilmarnock Maternity Home. It was so much quieter that Ayrshire Central Hospital and had a lovely atmosphere. The icing on the cake for me of course was delivering a baby there. The very same small hospital where I had entered the world. I had to wait quite a while past my supposed finishing time, but it was worth it.

My best friend, Alison, lived quite near me, and she had the use of her father's car during the week. Our tutor, Miss McGuire, was a lovely, mother hen sort of character. She had a friendly round face, and always wore her salt and pepper coloured hair in a rather loose bun. She often wore tartan skirts under her white lab coat, thick stockings and flat brogues.

She agreed that we could work together when we were out in the community, instead of me tramping around on foot or using public transport; we doubled our case load and travelled together in Alison's dad's car.

We were fitted with a navy-blue belted trench coat to wear over our thin, white, short-sleeved uniform, and given a matching blue hat. There was just enough room to wear a thin navy cardigan under the coat. Being cold was not an issue on the wards, they were always quite warm, but we were furnished with horrible-looking, royal blue jackets to wear when walking between wards, or when going to the restaurant, but never to be worn when working with patients.

At Ayrshire, Central, we also had the use of a voluminous, red-lined, long black cape.

Uniform policy in both hospitals was very strict. Hair either had to be above the collar or pinned up securely and tucked under our caps. The only jewellery allowed was a plain wedding band. Absolutely no nail polish, or long nails.

Alison and I agreed that the hat looked a bit limp and insipid. We decided that the only thing to do was stuff it with some toilet paper to give it a more structured and attractive shape. Each day we were on tenterhooks wondering if the multiple Kirby grips we used would be enough to keep the hat in place on top of our heads without letting any of the paper escape.

Working in the community was an absolute eye-opener for both of us. We had worked in the community during our general training of course, but not unsupervised. Nursing patients at home is so completely different to the hospital environment which is clean and controlled.

In a few homes, the floors and carpets could be so dirty that our shoes would stick to them.

We often decided against taking our coats off because there was nowhere clean enough to put them. We also became very adept at saying, 'No tea for me, thank you, I've just had one,' as we eyed dubious-looking kitchens and tea cups.

December 1981 had some of the coldest, snowiest weather since records began in the UK; it was the coldest December since 1890, and the snowiest since 1878.

One Friday afternoon, the air was thick with frost and almost took your breath away. Alison and I were out visiting our patients thankful for the clean, cosy homes we visited on our rounds which had glistening Christmas trees, hot coffee and home baking on offer.

Several new mums asked about taking baby out in the cold weather. Should they, or shouldn't they? Mothers and mothers-in-law often offered opinions about such things, but the new Mums sought our advice. We replied, parrot fashion, as taught in class, that fresh air was good for baby so long as he or she was well wrapped up.

When we returned to class on Monday morning Miss McGuire declared, with great aplomb, that anyone who had taken a baby out over the bitterly cold weekend needed their head looking at!

Alison and I looked at each other and a bout of nervous giggles ensued. We reassured each other that wise grandparents would have taken the upper hand and insisted that baby stayed firmly indoors.

Two other embarrassing events happened that bitterly cold December.

Firstly, I ran into my gran in town just after I had been allowed to finish early after a very poor turn out at the weekly antenatal clinic. Student midwives were often superfluous to requirements and told to, 'Take the rest of the afternoon off and don't let your tutors know about it.'

I got all my Christmas shopping done in record time that year. I adore Christmas, and the fact that the weather really looked the part made it idyllic and all the more enjoyable.

I bumped into Gran on King Street one afternoon; she took one look at my thin blue coat, thin tights, and she marched me into House of Fraser hosiery department, muttering, 'You'll catch your death of cold, lassie.'

She found, and bought me the thickest, and I thought, ugliest, pair of navy-blue woollen ribbed tights I had ever seen and sent me to the ladies' toilets there and then to put them on. I was mortified but did as I was told.

They turned out to be very comfortable and very warm, and oh, what a difference they made. I was so glad of them in the following weeks; Gran always knew best.

The other embarrassing incident that winter involved me, my brothers, the Mini Clubman and a Christmas tree.

I decided that our family should have a real tree for a change. Mum and Dad weren't too keen, claiming the needles would get everywhere, but I assured them that I would keep the tree watered and take full responsibility for it.

I asked Gran and Papa if I could borrow their car yet again (they owned the Mini, and looked after it like a baby. Papa had his own company car which I was not allowed to use). I thought that Jim and Alastair (six and ten years my junior respectively remember) would enjoy the whole tree-choosing festive experience.

My nervousness was palpable. Driving a borrowed, treasured, two-door Mini and using the multi-storey car park for the first time ever (out of sheer desperation, having been the source of amusement to pedestrians and annoyance to motorists while attempting to parallel park in a side street). I drove up to the booth, wound down my window, and found I couldn't reach the parking ticket which was being offered. Mortified, I got out of the car, ignoring the look of incredulity from the driver in the car behind me while the boys stated earnestly, 'That's not how Dad does it.' Not the best start to the day, but my excitement knew no bounds.

We went to a reputable florist, having been warned by Mum and Dad that if the needles dropped too quickly it would be our first and last real Christmas tree. It was larger than a Mini could comfortably cope with, but our enthusiasm was inexorable. We had already been to Woolworths to buy some shiny new decorations for it. Consumers were informed that Woolworths had 'the choice you want, at the prices you want to pay' and that everything they could possibly need for Christmas would be found in Woolworths. The adverts were star studded, Leslie Crowther perusing Polaroid instamatic cameras and television sets, Anita Harris handling handbags and hair driers. Tim Brook-Taylor selecting socks, Magnus Pyke considering a new calculator and Ed Stewart spinning records on the latest Hi-Fi, plus various sports personalities spraying themselves with Brut and Denim aftershaves. True to their word, it was like Aladdin's cave, packed with toys, games, records and cassettes, tins of Quality Street and Roses, a vast array of selection boxes, and of course Christmas decorations. Like all the other people who were out shopping on that grey day, we couldn't wait to get home. The boys sat on the back seat, the tree was propped up in the front, its resplendent pine-scented branches spewing unceremoniously into every available nook and cranny. Determined that my egress would be faultless after the entrance debacle and trying not to be distracted by the branches prickling my left hand (and my brothers giggling nervously in the back) I wound the window down as I approached the ticket booth and watched in horror as the ticket fell to the ground. I made to open the car door, but my resolve not to be caught out again, meant I parked so close to the booth that the car door couldn't open! In an instant, hooting and honking started, Christmas spirit vanishing into the now blue ether.

The car was so close to the booth, that the door wouldn't open. My brothers were in the back because the massive (well, massive for a Mini) tree was taking up the entire front seat, and then some.

I was by now in such a fluster and bright red with embarrassment that I can't really remember who retrieved the ticket; it may have been the occupant of the car behind or the ticket collector.

Suffice to say, it is now 2018, and December of 1981 was the last time I was in that particular car park. I have used a multi-storey car park since then of course; one particular visit presented me with another embarrassing situation. I was in Letchworth and had my two daughters and one of my future sons-in-law in the car. It was a Saab convertible, and I had the top down that day. I managed to get into a very tight space between another car and a pillar but decided that I needed to straighten the car up a bit to save face when I returned. I ended up with my door actually touching the pillar, the whole time my CD was belting out a rousing rendition of the 633 Squadron theme, which seemed to be ricocheting off the walls. It hadn't occurred to me to switch it off in my horror. I ended up calling out to a man who was a few cars away, much to the disgust of Jemma, my daughter, who said I was letting down all of womankind. He kindly helped me manoeuvre my way out, but to this day, whenever the girls or Andy hear stirring (especially military) tunes, they are referred to as 'good parking music' for Mum.

*

I passed my midwifery finals having survived the practical and oral exams at Rottenrow Hospital in Glasgow (what an awful name).

In May 1982 I could officially use RGN, SCM (registered general nurse, state certified midwife) after my name. My plain white cap now had a broad maroon stripe around it, and I was a staff midwife and very proud. My fiancé was waiting to hear about his position at Dounreay Nuclear Power Station; it had a prototype fast reactor known as a PFR. This highlighted the danger of abbreviations because to me a PFR was a pelvic floor repair.

In readiness of my fiancé's anticipated post, I went for an interview at The Dunbar Hospital in Thurso, Caithness, and was offered the post of staff midwife on the spot.

My post there was, to say the least, a baptism of fire…

CHAPTER 9

DUNBAR HOSPITAL THURSO

"You cannot understand what you have not experienced."

"Why aren't midwives the heroines of society that they should be? Why do they have such a low profile? They ought to be lauded to the skies, by everyone."

Jennifer Worth – *Call the Midwife, A Memoir of Birth, Joy and Hard Times.*

My fiancé and I got married in Crosshouse Parish Church on the 26th of June 1982. Our reception was held in the beautiful 18th-century Belleisle House Hotel in Alloway, Ayr. Sadly, it is another building which has been allowed to decay, but at the time of writing, plans are afoot to restore it to its former glory. The grounds and gardens were stunning and perfect for photographs.

We went to Paris for our honeymoon; I got a horrendous cold and felt very ill, but fortunately the football world cup was on the television for other half. We visited all the usual landmarks including the palace of Versailles, and strangely enough tended to eat Italian food almost every night. On the way home, we flew from Paris to London only to find there was a rail strike and we couldn't get a train back to Glasgow. I dipped into the last of my savings and bought flights from London to Glasgow so that we would be back in time for other half's graduation. He received his BSC (Hons), Mechanical

Engineering in Paisley surrounded by his proud family and his new wife.

Next came the long and arduous journey northward to Thurso and the start of our married life together. I was heartbroken to leave my family so far behind; the drive to Thurso took about eight hours and the roads at that time were far from ideal. We arrived late at night to our new home in Thorfinn Terrace. It was a wooden house, designed in Sweden to withstand the harshest weather nature could throw at it. I thought it was rather ugly, but it was undoubtedly warm inside with central heating powered by the coal fire which was enclosed and had a glass door, and it had double glazing. The décor was typical late 60s, early 70s; the sitting room had wallpaper which looked like a dry-stone wall, and the kitchen had worn orange and black lino. We had three bedrooms and a bathroom upstairs, a sitting-cum-dining room downstairs along with a toilet, kitchen, back porch and what I can only describe as an indoor shed and coal house. It was very well thought out, but oh did it need to be decorated.

*

I started work as a staff midwife at the Dunbar Hospital in Thurso on the 14th of July 1982.

Thurso is two hundred and ninety-seven miles from my parents' house. It seemed like the back of beyond to me. We could even see the Orkney Islands from our kitchen window. I had not lived away from home before, apart from the odd overnight stay in the nurses' home, and when I worked for George Hannah in Skelmorlie, so it was all very peculiar at times. I tended to work every weekend, much to my annoyance, and had Tuesdays and Wednesdays off. Theatre days were Mondays and Thursdays so that had a lot to do with the off-duty which was allocated to me. I felt very lonely at times. I was twenty-two years old but felt much older.

The town of Wick was about twenty miles away and was home to the nearest general hospital. John O'Groats was only nineteen miles away, and we would sometimes drive there for something to do if I wasn't working on the weekend. The nearest city to Thurso is Inverness, about one hundred and ten miles south. The journey to Inverness in the winter was dependent on the snow gates being open. Snow gates were deemed necessary after the brutal winter of 1978.

*

In 1978, snow tragically claimed the lives of three people in Caithness.

One man who survived, was salesman, Billy Sutherland. He was found inside his Mini Clubman, under fifteen feet of snow near the Ord of Caithness. He had set off three and a half days earlier from his home in Wick, heading for Helmsdale. He survived by managing to make a hole in the snow for air using an umbrella and by drinking melted snow. He used his cargo of women's hosiery to keep himself warm. The story made headlines all over the world.

Figure 14: *Scrabster Harbour*

Scrabster is a small village situated near to Thurso and it is well known for its harbour and fishing. Originally it was constructed as a deep-water anchorage, and it became the gateway to Shetland, Orkney, Scandinavia and the Faroe Islands. It was also used as the base for ferries which carried military explosives to Scapa Flow during World War Two.

It is very picturesque, and when we lived in Thurso, Scrabster had a fantastic restaurant called The Upper Deck, which commanded superb views of the harbour and offered the very best scotch beef fillet steak.

Every summer, the Royal Yacht *Britannia* would dock in the harbour. A magnificent launch would bring the Queen and Prince Philip ashore, plus any other royals who were holidaying with them at Balmoral, such as Princess Anne and her children, Princess Diana, and Prince Charles with William and Harry, to name but a few. They were met by the Queen Mother, and then taken to her Highland home, the Castle of Mey. It was all very informal by royal standards and was quite a spectacle for royal watchers.

In the summer months, we always had plenty of visitors coming to stay with us, so it was good to have the castle on our list of places to visit, along with the Caithness Glass Factory, and John O'Groats. The Castle of Mey gardens are beautiful, and the Queen Mother always attended the annual Mey Highland Games.

As for me, to say I felt cut off from the rest of the world is an understatement. I felt very homesick and not at all at home in my new environment.

Being a newly qualified midwife, I was used to a vast support network of senior nursing staff, paediatricians and obstetricians. Things at The Dunbar Hospital were different. Very different.

Mr. Alexander Dunbar, who resided in Scrabster until his death in 1859, left the sum of £10,000 in his will requesting that it should be allowed to accumulate interest for twenty-one years, and that the money should be used to build a general hospital.

The stone-built, Baronial-style hospital was completed and opened in 1885.

Figure 15: *Dunbar Hospital, Thurso, Caithness*

When I started my post as staff midwife on the fourteenth of July 1982, the hospital consisted of a ward for gynaecological patients at one end of the building, and a ward for obstetric patients at the other with various single rooms dotted around. The two main ward areas were connected by a long corridor. There was an operating theatre, kitchens and dining room on one side of the corridor, offices and the single side rooms on the other.

The nurse changing rooms were in a separate portacabin-style annex just off the car park, as were the x-ray and physiotherapy departments.

At the back of the main hospital, was another stone-built building which housed the outpatient department and a small Casualty department which was unmanned out with normal office hours.

This meant that a nurse, usually from the gynae ward, had to fetch the keys and go over to open up the doors, and receive the patients who arrived for emergency treatment, mostly late evening and in the wee small hours of the morning. Once an extremely drunk man was brought to us in the boot of a car so that he wouldn't vomit all over the back seat. He was dumped unceremoniously on the ground outside the entrance; try dealing with that scenario on your own in the middle of the night.

Obviously, this was less than ideal, especially when you realise that normal staffing levels were usually kept to one trained nurse and one auxiliary nurse per shift on the gynae ward, and the same in the maternity section, although, we had extra staff on occasions, and on operating days.

We had one consultant obstetrician, Doctor Farquhar, who did not live in, and who worked office hours with quite a bit of give and take on his part. He carried out ward rounds, ran his outpatient clinics, and operated two days per week. Operating lists consisted of gynaecological procedures, for example, hysterectomies, and elective caesarean sections. We also had on-call staff to cover emergencies.

As I mentioned, for me, it was a case of hitting the ground running, and trying to circumnavigate the huge learning curve I found myself faced with.

You may be wondering, how many babies could we expect way up there in that sparsely populated part of Scotland?

Well, it was not as sparsely populated as you might imagine.

As well as Dounreay Nuclear Power Plant, run by the United Kingdom Atomic Energy Authority (UKAEA), there were two US Naval Communications Stations situated at Forss and West Murkle, just outside Thurso.

The naval stations provided facilities for the US Naval Command to relay command and control messages to vessels at sea. At their peak, they employed over two hundred personnel.

The UKAEA used the site at Dounreay for its Prototype Fast Reactor. It was built on the site of a World War Two airfield called RAF Station Dounreay and was remote to say the least. It was an imposing sight in a sci-fi sort of way with its 139-foot (42m) steel sphere dominating the landscape.

In 1960, a purpose-built Apprentice Training School was added. Also, the Ministry of Defence (MOD) Vulcan Naval Reactor Test Establishment was housed there, bringing the total number of reactors to five. Three managed by UKAEA, and two by the MOD. In 1978. It was decided to offer public tours. Guides took great pleasure in telling people, 'You are now standing on top of the reactor that is generating 600Mw of thermal power.' UKAEA also employed their own armed police presence to help safeguard the plutonium and uranium held within.

All of the above meant jobs, and plenty of them, resulting in a high percentage of young men, women and children living in the area.

My first few deliveries were tense affairs after the honeymoon period (pardon the pun) was over and it was just me and an auxiliary nurse present. No senior staff or doctors in the building to call upon for advice or support. Of course, they were at the end of a telephone, but that is not quite the same thing.

The auxiliaries were amazing nurses. Years of experience and oodles of common sense to boot.

I soon discovered that I was so pre-occupied with the technicalities and niceties of the labour and delivery that I forgot to look at the clock at the actual time of birth. It was usually the first question the new dad asked, and of course, it was recorded for posterity and legal reasons. I quickly learned to delegate this task to the dad-to-be, it made him feel useful and got me out of a potentially tricky situation.

More than once a new dad-to-be would keel over and fall in a heap on the floor. If this happened at a crucial part of the proceedings, we had to leave him there to his own devices after a cursory look to make sure there were no major injuries and that he was still breathing. With just two of us in attendance we had to concentrate on Mum and baby.

As well as women in labour, we had a ward full of postnatal mums and babies to look after. The mums were mostly self-sufficient, but they were the responsibility of the midwife on duty, nonetheless.

As a midwife, you are expected to give bathing demonstrations, demonstrate how to mix up formula milk, and assist any mum who is having difficulty with breast feeding.

One bathing demonstration sticks in my mind because of a remark made to me afterwards.

A woman, who was to become a good friend, told me after I had expertly bathed the baby, and fitted it snugly into its pin-free, terry towelling nappy using a series of flaps and tucks, that she, and the other mums, looked on, bewildered and somewhat in awe.

After I left the room, apparently, they started to laugh uncontrollably, because they had tried and failed the safety-pinless nappy many times with disastrous results. No wonder disposables became popular.

When visiting hour was approaching, the nurses would fetch the babies into the glass-fronted nursery where the babies slept at night. The window ran the length of the nursery, allowing light and vision into the nursery. One very busy evening, I am ashamed to say, Baby A was inadvertently put into Baby B's cot. This is not as bad as it sounds in that each baby wore two identity bracelets and they would have been switched back immediately, except that a set of proud grandparents appeared in front of the window and started to take photographs of the labelled bassinette. Right name, wrong baby. As soon as was humanly possible, the still-sleeping babies were returned to their respective cots. Nobody noticed the inadvertent switch, but I do feel a bit guilty when I think that there might be a blurry, taken through glass, flashlight-filled photo of that baby in an album somewhere.

Thankfully, most deliveries were straightforward and needed very little intervention.

If complications did arise, it usually meant a transfer to Raigmore Hospital in Inverness, either by road (if the snow gates were open) or by helicopter. It also meant being called in if you were off duty to escort mother and baby.

Commonly, everything was straightforward. I rarely used a foetal monitor, I preferred to carry my trusty Pinard stethoscope in my pocket to check the foetal heartbeat.

When a woman was ready for the labour room, we would put an electric blanket in her bed so that it was warm and toasty for her return. This was a nice touch I had not come across before and was always much appreciated by the newly delivered mums.

The food in the hospital was second to none. It was simply amazing.

Where do I start?

Every Thursday, the cook would make several curries from

scratch, with all the accompaniments. I believe this was a special request from the visiting anaesthetist who came to The Dunbar for the Thursday theatre list.

The cook made ice cream to die for, and provided warm, home-baked rolls, called butteries, every morning. Homemade jams, and biscuits and cakes, roast dinners, stews, fish, amazing salads and the most delicious soups. Most definitely, not typical hospital food.

Working as a midwife at The Dunbar was hard but rewarding work. I am very proud to tell you that quite a few babies were named Jacqueline in my honour, and one baby boy was named after my husband.

A late shift ended at ten thirty, later if there had been a delivery because there was a mountain of paperwork to complete before we could go home.

I cycled to and from work quite a bit at that time; we had a car, but my husband needed it for the journey to Dounreay.

One morning, the house telephone rang, it was my OH telling me he had been involved in an accident. In short, our Fiat X-19 had skidded on an icy patch of road and was lodged under a bus. How he escaped unscathed I will never know, but he did, and apart from the usual insurance documents to sort out, and the inconvenience of not having a car, I didn't really give it much thought. The car had proved to be a big hit with our new puppy, Jilly. She loved nothing better than to wrap herself around OH's shoulders when he was driving, resembling a furry bobbing scarf.

We got a puppy quite unexpectedly. The hospital secretary, Essie, came into work one day, rather distraught. She lived on a farm, and the sheep dog had given birth to a litter of puppies, which her husband had 'got rid of' or so he thought. But, two puppies had survived, and Essie was anxious to find homes for them.

I will never forget going into her sitting room to find two big-eyed, jet-black puppies.

It was almost eleven o'clock at night, I had just finished work. One puppy was quite boisterous and confident. The other was quiet, and rather withdrawn. With gentle coaxing, the shy pup came forward, and that was it. Love at first sight. She came home with us that evening. When it came to be choosing a name, we were a bit stuck. I was reading a book by Jilly Cooper at the time, and there it was, in black and white, the perfect name. Jilly.

We were totally unprepared for a puppy but managed to convert the cardboard box which had contained our new portable colour television set, into a bed. We lined it with newspapers and blankets.

Jilly howled pitifully for most of the night. I was beside myself with worry, not least because I was on duty again at seven thirty.

Everyone at work pulled together to get me through that first day. I got a lift home at lunchtime to check that Jilly was okay and to let her out into the garden. In hindsight, it wasn't the best start a puppy could ask for, but we managed, and she was much loved.

*Jilly at Thorfinn terrace
Thurso*

Jilly was a beautiful, good-natured dog. That said, she had a penchant for emptying the bin in the kitchen, scattering the contents all over the floor. The first night we left her alone in the house for a couple of hours, we returned to find the plant in the hall was missing; the bamboo floor standing pot was conspicuously empty.

I knew I had brought a loaf out of the freezer to defrost and left it on the kitchen table – that was also missing. In the sitting room, a dish which had contained some chocolates including a Terry's Chocolate Orange, was also completely empty.

Jilly was very pleased to see us, and she waddled around wagging her tail. OH was annoyed with her, but, I was very concerned. Her abdomen was quite distended, and I feared the worst.

As luck would have it, apart from a lot of flatulence and quite a bit of vomiting, thankfully, she was perfectly fine.

The morning after the car accident, I set off to work on foot. My head was spinning, and I felt nauseated and ill. I got about halfway to work but decided that I should get back home to bed.

When I got home, Jilly was delighted to see me, her tail wagging excitedly, so glad to have company again. I called in sick and went straight to bed with Jilly snuggled in beside me happy and contented.

I must have fallen into a deep sleep, and awoke with a start as the telephone, which was downstairs in the hall, started to ring. Jilly, who was still cuddled up beside me, sat up too, and followed me downstairs.

The next thing I can remember was lying on the floor with Jilly licking my face.

What on earth made me lie down here? I thought to myself, and then I spied the receiver for the telephone dangling in mid-air. Then I could make out a voice asking if I was okay.

I managed to reach out and grab the receiver, and then felt an overwhelming urge to throw up. I mumbled something along those lines into the mouthpiece, and just made it to the downstairs loo in time.

Later that morning, Sister Connie Smith arrived at the door, having been given a lift to our house in an ambulance no less. She was in full uniform, and was wearing a long black cape; it must have looked very dramatic to the neighbours.

The doctor was called in by Connie, and he decided it was a reaction to the car accident the day before, and prescribed tranquilisers for me.

When I went back to work the next day, a lovely nurse called Mary Ness said, 'Don't take any more of those tablets. I know what is wrong with you, and it has nothing to do with the car accident.'

I never quite lived it down. The midwife who had no idea she was pregnant.

Exactly one year to the day that I had started work at the Dunbar hospital, Jemma was born on the 14th of July 1983. It was my gran's 70th birthday.

I adored my new baby girl, and adored being a mother, but friends and family alike mistakenly thought that because I was a midwife that I would take motherhood in my stride. Of course, the practicalities like changing nappies and handling Jemma with confidence were second nature to me, but the emotions involved with having my very own baby took me very much by surprise and knocked me sideways. I had postnatal depression, although it went undiagnosed for a year. Going back to work was unthinkable. I wanted to look after my baby by myself. I wanted to protect my daughter from everything and everyone. The only person I trusted to look after Jemma to allow OH and I a night out was Tina, my friend and the midwife who had delivered her. I made sure the snowy-white terry towelling nappies were on the line first thing in the morning. No one would say I wasn't coping if they saw that I was so well organised.

I also went to the weekly baby clinic early so that I could be seen first and not talk to the other mothers, making excuses, saying I was in a mad rush to be somewhere. When I called home, I would tell everyone about Jemma's latest achievements, for example, 'she sat up by herself' and then, when I put the phone down I would sob uncontrollably.

In my opinion, OH was ambitious, enthusiastic and worked hard to build his career. He was often away on courses, and, having been a student with all the restraints being a student brings, he made the most of having money and leisure time for the first time in several years by socialising.

It was not a happy time for me. I adored my baby daughter, but I did not enjoy life in general. Rightly or wrongly, I blamed Thurso and couldn't wait for the day that we would be able to live somewhere else.

I did go back to work when Jemma was about two. It was a temporary post, to cover someone's maternity leave. Six months of night duty, not my ideal choice of shift; so much for my vow never to work nights again. It was during this stint of night duty that Live Aid was broadcast on television.

The event was organised by Bob Geldof and Midge Ure to raise money for the famine-stricken people in Ethiopia. Over seventy-five acts performed – Eric Clapton, Madonna, U2 and Queen to name but a few. It was a huge deal! The concert started in Wembley Stadium in London and continued at the JFK Stadium in Philadelphia and other venues around the world. The concerts were linked by satellite and broadcast to more than a billion viewers in 110 countries. Phil Collins even flew by Concorde to perform in Philadelphia after he had performed at Wembley. It was amazing at the time.

That Saturday night, the 13th of July 1985, the night before Jemma's second birthday, I managed to watch snippets during my breaks, on the small television which had been set up especially for the event in the staff dining room. It was quite a spectacle; world-famous acts and thousands of people enjoying themselves. I don't think I ever felt quite so cut off from the rest of the world as I did that night sitting in the dining room of the little Highland hospital alone. I have since learned that there was a certain policeman on duty at the concert in Wembley Stadium, helping to control the 70,000-strong crowd, who would become my husband many years later!

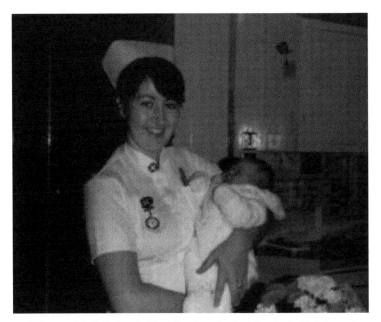

Figure 16: *Me in the Dunbar hospital with a baby I delivered*

CHAPTER 10

NORTH BERWICK

"The cure for anything is salt water: sweat, tears or the sea."

- Isak Dinesen

We moved from Thurso in February 1986. OH had been offered a position at Torness Nuclear Power Station in Dunbar, East Lothian. As we drove away from Thorfinn Terrace I did not even take a second glance at the house. I couldn't wait to get away from it.

To begin with we moved into rented accommodation in Dunbar, a seaside town in East Lothian, not to be confused with the hospital in Caithness). I loved the fact that we were now only about two hours away from our families, and that we were so close to Edinburgh.

I was pregnant with Lisa, and she was due on May the first. my grandfather's birthday, but we all know lightening doesn't strike twice.

We spent a lot of time at weekends sightseeing and particularly liked the town of North Berwick which wasn't too far away.

North Berwick is a picturesque seaside town, with many beautiful old properties from its heyday when it was known as 'The Biarritz of The North'.

One weekend while I was reading our local paper, the *East Lothian Courier*, I spied a property for sale – four bedrooms, kitchen, sitting room, dining room, study, a bathroom and a toilet. It also boasted many original features, such as fireplaces, ornate cornice, and the original staircase. It was on the market for an unbelievably low price.

Figure 17: *Warrender, North Berwick*

"Where are the turrets? Even our house has turrets."
— Jemma, age four, visiting Edinburgh Castle

We made an appointment to view.

We drove to North Berwick on a perfect spring day; the views over the Firth of Forth were spectacular. As luck would have it, my gran was staying with us for a couple of weeks, and we valued her opinion, so she got settled into the back of the car beside Jemma who was safely strapped into her car seat.

We drove from Dunbar along the coast road, passing the stunning Tantallon Castle, and had impressive views of the Bass Rock on that sunny, blue-skied day. The sea was quite calm, but there were rows of 'white horses' gently frothing onto the shores beneath us.

We drove though North Berwick's narrow high street, with its quaint buildings and shops. I immediately felt at home. We headed for the west end. Driving up Station Road, we could see the railway station to the left and Dirleton Avenue straight ahead. The sign on the road to our right said, 'York Road'. We turned right and drove down York Road. The property was instantly recognisable from the small black and white photograph that had been printed in the newspaper. I gazed up at Warrender House, and immediately fell in love with it.

I was to find out, after quite a bit of research, that it had first been built as a private dwelling, then became 'Warrender Hotel'. It was also allegedly used as a Polish officers' mess during World War Two according to several neighbours, but I haven't managed to find any proof.

Sometime in the 1940s, the house was divided up into four flats; the bottom two were split again in the 1960s making a total of six flats within Warrender House. Two larger properties at the top, and four smaller at the bottom. The flat we were viewing housed the turrets at the top of the building.

Entering the large, heavy, main front door from York Road, there was a typical Victorian tiled entrance vestibule. Above the door, was a small window, on which was painted in gold the name 'Warrender'.

A second large, white-painted door, which had elegant glass panels, led into you into a small hallway.

There were five other doors in hallway – three front entrance doors and two cupboard doors. The cupboard which was to become ours, had been a coal house, but was now clean and had a small piece of carpet on the floor. The property was large but lacked storage space; presumably none was needed on the upper floors when the house was built, all of the storage space being housed in the lower floors and basements for servants to use, so this cupboard was going to be well utilised. The cupboard next to it was still being used as a coal house.

When we rang the bell, a petite, rather frail-looking lady came to the door and invited us in. She seemed to be delighted that we had a two-year-old and another baby on the way. She told us that the building needed young blood.

She introduced herself as Evarild Chisnall, and showed us into the sitting room, which was furnished with the same maroon-coloured carpet as the hall and stairs. Straight in front of us, the stunning turret windows were adorned with shiny gold-coloured curtains which were long but did not quite reach the floor (I came to loathe those curtains). On the left-hand wall, stood a large mantelpiece which although was an original feature, was covered with, what had once been white but was now yellowing, gloss paint. The actual fire surround and hearth had been tiled with rather ugly, 1960s-style beige tiles. The only source of heat in the room was a dismal-looking electric fire. There was a picture rail, and a very deep skirting board.

A single bed, neatly made up, was situated along the far-right wall opposite the fireplace. Mrs. Chisnall explained that she slept there because it was warmer than the bedroom next door and that she never ventured upstairs these days. The ceiling was high with an almost geometrical-style ornate cornice. After making some appreciative noises, we moved into what would become our dining room.

The 'dining room' had a very large wooden bed, an impressive Edwardian wardrobe and a dressing table. The carpet was a pale green colour and was covered with pale pink roses. The fireplace looked almost identical to the one in the sitting room, but the uprights of the mantle had been wallpapered and painted white to match the painted wallpaper which was on sections of the large wardrobe.

The curtains were a mossy green colour, and were neither long nor short; they also looked very flimsy. There were stunning views over the Firth of Forth out of the two back windows. There was also a window on the left-hand wall as you entered the room, next to the wardrobe, offering a lovely view of the Marine Hotel and Cromwell Road. The ceiling was high and featured an ornate cornice, which was thickly covered with numerous coats of paint which masked the once fine acorn details.

The kitchen had, dull, worn, red linoleum on the uneven floor, a single sink tucked into the far-left corner, a window, with window seat, which overlooked York Road, and a cooker. It also had a large fireplace, and obligatory high ceiling and cornice.

Mrs. Chisnall explained, pointing to the left out of the kitchen window, that the property had a large garden, which was accessed by leaving by the front door and walking along York Road for a couple of yards and entering it through the garden gate.

We stood in the hall and looked down the stairwell towards the front door.

From the front door, the stone staircase curved up to the right, leading to the first small landing just outside the bathroom door. The bathroom housed a large cast-iron bath standing on ornate legs. The room had a (in my opinion disproportionately) high ceiling, and a large window.

Years later, when we sent the doors to have various layers of paint removed, we saw the outline of the number thirteen; the bathroom had obviously been room thirteen when Warrender was a hotel. This proved to be rather poignant.

The staircase continued from the first-floor hallway in a spectacular curve up to the second floor.

Again, there was a small landing which housed the door to the toilet which also had an incredibly high ceiling and a skylight window. It was a high-level toilet, with the cistern mounted high on the wall with an exposed pipe joining it to the toilet pan. It had a long chain with a wooden handle which you pulled to flush the toilet and there was a small sink in the corner. There were a couple of more steps to the right of the toilet door which led up to the second hallway off which was a study full of Mr. William Chisnall's book collection, some of which he had written himself. They are not worth anything in monitory terms, but I still treasure them to this day. They included the complete works of Shakespeare and an entire set of the *Encyclopaedia Britannica* dated 1926.

Next door to the study, was a room which had obviously been a kitchenette or scullery. It housed an old lead water tank and a couple of large chipped Belfast sinks and was directly above the kitchen, overlooking the front of the house. What would become the master bedroom, was being used as a dining room and it looked elegant with the turret windows in spite of the 1960s-style psychedelic swivel chairs dotted around the room.

There were two further bedrooms at the back, but it was obvious that they had originally been adjoined as one room once upon a time.

The stair carpet was held in place with thin brass stair rods. The painted wooden hand rail was beautifully curved, and there was a dado rail. A large cupola window allowed natural light to pour in, illuminating the whole stairwell.

The painted white doors had solid, round wooden handles, also painted white, trimmed with brass. The light switches were also made of brass.

The only rooms which did not have a fireplace were the upstairs toilet and the bedroom overlooking Cromwell Road (the one which had once been part of the bedroom overlooking the Firth of Forth).

The carpets and curtains had seen better days. Furniture included a large dining room table and chairs with scuffed and sunken leather seat pads, a large bookcase, and some charming little coffee tables. The downside was that the dining table had been covered with wood-effect Formica, and the legs had been painted black. Ditto with the coffee tables, only they had white Formica tops. There was a large, menacing-looking trunk which eventually was put to good use as a toy box (after I had plucked up the courage to open it).

The bedrooms at the back of the property were painted a matte, muddy-looking green colour. There were posters on the walls held in place with drawing pins, and it was plain to see, that the wall behind one of the posters was white. We were to discover that all the posters had been painted around, as was the bookcase and several other pieces of furniture which were placed against a wall. It was obvious that this would not be an easy undertaking, but it was perfect for us. It was affordable because of the flaws. We could live in it while we renovated it ourselves when money and time allowed. It had massive potential and we felt that we were up to the challenge. We could envisage what it could look like in the future.

Mrs. Chisnall explained that a man had viewed the property with a view to housing his antiques and art collections. He had no need for central heating, but Mrs. Chisnall had other ideas. She wanted a family to move in and love it just as she had done. All the other residents in the building were retired. Now that Mr. Chisnall had passed away, she planned to sell up and move closer to her daughter and grandchildren, but she wanted to know that her property was passing to a family who would update and love it. After what seemed like an age, all the 'T's were crossed, and the 'I's were dotted.

It was finally ours.

*

Lisa was born on a very sunny and warm first of May 1986, my grandfather's birthday, so lightening does indeed strike twice. I had sailed through my second pregnancy. I had the obligatory morning, noon and night sickness just as I had had with Jemma, but other than that it was business as usual. I only just made it to the hospital in time to give birth, but, unfortunately too late for analgesics other than gas and air via a mask which I just could not tolerate on my face. I hadn't planned a natural childbirth, but it was surprisingly uneventful. Lisa arrived safe and sound and was an extremely good baby. During my pregnancy I had worried that it would not be possible to love another child as much as I loved Jemma, but as soon as Lisa was born and was placed in my arms looking at me with her big dark eyes, everything fell into place just as it should. She was perfect.

Only one thing blighted this happy time for me. The newspaper headlines and the news being broadcast on television and on the radio.

On April 26th 1986, the world's worst nuclear accident (to date) happened at the Chernobyl plant near Pripyat, Ukraine, in the Soviet Union. An explosion and fire in the No. 4 reactor sent radioactivity into the atmosphere. The Soviet government eventually released a statement acknowledging that there had been a nuclear accident after Finland, Sweden and Denmark had reported abnormally high radioactivity levels in their skies.

The Chernobyl accident happened during a test to see how the plant would operate if it lost power. Plant operators made several mistakes, creating an unstable environment in the reactor core. However, they proceeded with the experiment, shutting down safety systems that would be lost during a power outage, including the turbine system that provided cooling water. With the flow reduced, the cooling water in the reactor began to boil and turn to steam. Operators tried to reinsert rods to slow and control the nuclear reaction, but a design flaw in the control rods caused them to jam. The steam was a likely cause of an explosion in the reactor, which, in turn, caused a second explosion seconds later. Debris from the explosion caused a number of fires around the plant. It released radioactive smoke into the atmosphere that spread over the western Soviet Union and Europe. The radioactive release into the atmosphere has been approximated at 400 times the size of the atomic bomb dropped on Hiroshima. That said, the disaster could have been worse if it had not been for the actions and reactions of Pripyat firefighters who were able to put out the fires before they caused explosions in the other three reactors. Anyone living within a thirty-mile (48km) radius of the power plant had to leave their homes and move to safety.

Immediately after the accident occurred, radioactive plumes formed a radioactive cloud which was released into the atmosphere. This radioactive cloud drifted not only over Russia, Belarus and the Ukraine, but also over most of Europe and as far away as Canada.

Almost 9,000 British farms were placed under restrictions.

Advice issued to calm public fears only exacerbated them. Heavy rain in April and May in 1986 saturated higher ground with disturbing quantities of radioactive caesium and iodine. The authorities reacted by imposing a blanket ban on the sale of all farm animals and panic spread throughout the UK.

Anxious members of the public inundated the Ministry of Agriculture, Food and Fisheries with telephone calls for reassurance and guidance.

Whilst the accident had a huge impact in Britain as a whole, it especially hit all those involved with the running of nuclear power plants very hard indeed. The public became suspicious of and somewhat hostile towards nuclear power. I expect that there were numerous meetings and conferences analysing the accident and making plans for the future, but OH did not talk about them at home. I knew from being married to a nuclear engineer that safety within nuclear plants was paramount and second to none. OH tried to reassure me, but as a mother of an infant and a toddler, I decided to take my own precautions. I bought bottled water and powdered milk, assuming that they had been bottled and manufactured prior to the accident. I was breast feeding so I also drank the bottled and powdered beverages and refused to take Jemma and Lisa out if it was raining (I did not buy lamb for several years).

In total, 344 Welsh farms were put under restrictions, with animals' radiation levels monitored before they were allowed to be sold at market.

The number of affected animals peaked in 1992, but some still recorded higher levels of caesium as recently as 2011. We now know, that although iodine-131 has a relatively short half-life compared to other radioactive isotopes, iodine-131 made its way through the food chain through a milk-to-consumer pathway; 95% of iodine-131 was ingested through milk shortly after the disaster. Communities were mostly unaware of the contamination being deposited in the soil and of the transforming capabilities of radiation into other food sources.

Through the consumption of milk, many children received abnormal amounts of radiation exposure.

There are numerous articles on the internet which have been published in national newspapers explaining what is thought to have happened that day in April 1986, and about the legacy Chernobyl has left behind.

*

We moved into Warrender when Lisa was about six weeks old. Two house moves, a birth and a nuclear disaster in a matter of a few months was not ideal, but we coped. Just.

*

The first night we spent in our new home was exciting, enlightening and if truth be told a bit daunting. There were no curtains in our room, so we systematically went around each of the turreted windows, fourteen in all, and taped black bin liners up for some privacy. We were so high up, that there really wasn't much need, but it seemed like the right thing to do at the time.

I must admit to having some doubts as the reality of what we were about to undertake kicked in.

'What have we done?' we chortled nervously in unison as we lay in bed looking at our makeshift blinds.

I bathed the girls in front of the electric heater in the sitting room; everywhere else was freezing cold, so we also made use of several paraffin heaters Mrs. Chisnall had left behind. We put Lisa's cot and Jemma's bed in the same room, right next to ours, choosing the room which seemed to be the brightest and least oppressive. Jilly slept on the floor in our room.

We embarked on what was to be our routine for years to come. OH working at the power station by day, me looking after two children, the house and garden. Our evenings and weekends were spent carrying out renovations, restoration and redecoration but we managed to have fun family times too, and it was very rewarding.

During the early days in North Berwick I did the weekly shop in the local Co-op, which meant pushing the pram up Station Hill loaded with bags on the tray underneath, Jemma sitting on top and Lisa lying in it. Not for the faint hearted.

Jemma started nursery school and ballet classes where she met Lauren who is one of her best friends to this day. Lauren's parents, Nicola and Geoff Hailstone, became good friends of ours too. Over the coming years Nicola and I helped each other with the school run, making sure Jemma, Lisa, Lauren and Charlotte got to school on time and with the correct books, musical instruments etc., and we all spent many an evening enjoying dinner parties and family days out. We still laugh about a dream I had when Nicola was expecting her third child. I told Nicola and Geoff that I dreamed that they were having a boy and that they would call him Walnut. They did have a boy, but wisely called him George.

*

We had agreed with Mrs. Chisnall when we bought the house that she could leave any unwanted furniture behind. Anything that we couldn't use, we would get rid of ourselves. The house we had moved from was much smaller, so we were very happy about this arrangement. We needed a skip for the renovations, so a few bits of furniture could be disposed of quite easily.

Eventually, all the boxes were unpacked. The dining table and chairs which had been left behind by Mrs. Chisnall were moved downstairs to the dining room, the bedroom furniture she left was moved upstairs, surplus beds were gotten rid of, and our new home began to resemble what we had envisaged when we first stepped inside.

I am embarrassed and ashamed to admit that we disposed of our large cast-iron bath with its ornate claw ball legs. It had seen better days, was worn and stained and we had no idea that it could be re-enamelled. We didn't even try to sell it, but I am not sure there would have been many takers at that time… would there? We had our hearts set on a large corner bath. Well, it was the 80s after all.

We pulled out the bedroom fireplaces and the kitchen fireplace. They were extremely heavy and unwieldly. The ample floor boards seemed to be permanently propped up against the walls while plumbing and electrical work was carried out by OH in the evenings, ably assisted by me once the girls were in bed. I became a dab hand with a blow torch and flux. The house resembled a building site and had a permanent layer of black dust over everything.

I decided to investigate what was underneath the wallpaper on the dining room fireplace. I scraped at the paper and paint and eventually revealed beautiful grey marble underneath. Out came the paint stripper. I was elated by my discovery. This led to the sitting room fireplace receiving the same treatment, it turned out to be black and not so ornate, but impressive, nonetheless.

Spurred on by the fireplace success, I removed the Formica from the dining room table to see what delights lay underneath. It was a bit of a mess, not least because it had been scraped and sanded before 'Evo stick' glue had been applied to attach the Formica. I carefully treated any damaged wood with filler and painstakingly painted the filled patches with wood stain to match the existing wood (which looked to me like walnut) to the best of my limited ability. I then took all the black paint off the chair legs using yet more paint stripper (I did not think to use a mask; health and safety was not what it is today) and polished the leather seats. If I had spent thousands of pounds on a new dining table and chairs I could not have been more delighted.

One painting incident sticks firmly in my mind.

We had chosen a colour of paint, for the sitting room, which had to be mixed and blended. This was done in the shop, and the lid was returned to the can of what had once been white paint. These shops also add clips to make sure the lid is reattached securely with good reason.

I was getting ready to take Jemma to nursery one afternoon and rushed to the loo before setting off on the rather lengthy uphill walk. I must have been so energetic and fit in those days, pushing the pram up hill and down dale, walking Jilly, looking after the garden, and helping OH with the substantial house renovations. Not forgetting, washing the windows inside and out (we couldn't get a window cleaner who would tackle them because they were so high up) and hand brushing the stair carpet because the hoover wouldn't reach. I also did the odd shift in a local nursing home, but I am going off at a tangent yet again.

When I came back into the sitting room to fetch the girls, I found a huge puddle of paint right in the middle of the floor (but not so central that it could be covered with a rug, as I discovered). Jemma was frantically using her toy Hoover to try and mop the gloopy paint up but merely succeeded in making paint wheel marks all around the room. Lisa, who was walking by this time, was jumping into the paint gleefully shouting, 'Puddle!' wearing her new start-rite shoes which had just cost, what to us at that time was, a small fortune.

I ran to the kitchen, got a bottle of washing up liquid and squirted the green liquid soap onto the paint and rubbed at it with a sponge. This action resulted in what looked like a quadrupling of the paint and soap mixture, it seemed to froth and foam and develop rather attractive big bubbles.

Right in the middle of this grand melee, the phone rang, it was OH to confirm that he would be working late. This was often the case, so much so, his work colleagues used to joke that I needed to show Jilly photos of him in case she thought he was an intruder. He was dedicated to his career and was often on call. Overtime was a double-edged sword. When he was at work, he couldn't get on with the renovations. He was doing all the work himself and designed the heating system and kitchen. But overtime was necessary if we were to proceed with buying the materials we required to complete it.

'I don't think so,' I replied, and did the only sensible thing I could and headed for the nursery with the girls leaving the mound of paint bubbles behind me.

After what seemed like an age, we got a lovely new carpet courtesy of the insurance company. They sent someone to try and clean it with no success, but I must say that was furthest from my mind at the time.

Figure 18: *Warrender, me with Jemma and Lisa, 1989*

CHAPTER 11

FAMILY LIFE

"When I was a boy of fourteen, my father was so ignorant I could hardly stand to have the old man around. But when I got to be twenty-one, I was astonished at how much the old man had learned in seven years."

- Mark Twain

Figure 19: *View from bedroom window, Warrender*

I loved North Berwick. It was idyllic to live so close to the beach, literally a stone's throw from the house and across the golf course. I also enjoyed finding out about the history of the town and our house.

I read an article written in 1906 which said: 'The Duke of Cambridge and Lord and Lady Hardinge are staying at Warrenders Hotel'.

Beth Masterton was one of our new neighbours. She was a lovely, gentle woman who lived alone in the flat next door to ours on the two uppermost floors. She eventually confided that her home was too big for her, but she did not want to sell because Warrender was filled with memories of her late husband both inside and out. Beth's sitting room had a balcony which looked directly onto the sea. The room was filled with chintzy furniture and side tables. One wall was dominated by a marble-topped table groaning with crystal glasses and decanters full of whisky, brandy and gin. Beth and her friends hosted bridge parties and Beth would go to Jenner's in Edinburgh to stock up with biscuits, crackers, cheeses and other delights when it was her turn. Beth still had her kitchenette upstairs as ours had once been. She also had a fascinating hand-painted mural on the wall of her ground-floor staircase. I was to discover that her staircase, also an original feature, was a mirror image of ours, complete with archways which I reckoned connected the two areas of the now separated house. Beth's bathroom was huge. It had a Victorian wash stand complete with a large jug and basin. It was for decoration only, but it had obviously been well used in the past. There was no central heating, only electric and paraffin heaters, but it was always quite toasty and comfortable.

Our other neighbours were Arthur and Ella Cruttenden, a charming elderly couple who must have wondered, in trepidation, what life was going to be like with a family consisting of an almost three-year-old, a new baby and a dog moving in upstairs. Ella had devised a system where a post card would be passed to me, then Beth and then back to her on a weekly basis. The holder of the card would use old-fashioned solid floor polish and an extremely heavy buffing brush to polish the original tiles in the entrance vestibule, keeping them looking pristine. Down in Arthur and Ella's property, original meat hooks could be seen on the ceiling in the basement kitchen. They also had what I believed to have been a servants' staircase, and masses of storage space which I envied.

I am delighted to say I keep in touch with Christine, their daughter, who now lives there.

Angela and Roger Kent had their own entrance at the side of the house, as did Cecil and Margaret Addison on the opposite side. There was another resident, but she rented out her property, so the occupants were always changing.

Mr. Struth, our elderly local butcher, told me that he remembered delivering meat to Warrender when he was a boy using what was now Angela and Roger's front door. He said the cook was very scary indeed and that she had several spiky whiskers on her chin.

I managed to track down a copy of the blueprints used when the house was first converted into four flats. Sadly, I no longer have them.

One day, while I was visiting Margaret in her basement flat, I cheekily asked to see inside the cupboard in her sitting room. I had noticed on the plans that there had been a staircase there; she opened the door, and lo and behold there it was, the remains of a staircase, now leading nowhere. I was delighted to find it.

Margaret loved to pick rhubarb from her garden and make rhubarb and ginger jam which she would share with all the other residents. Margaret was a graduate of The Sorbonne in Paris and spoke fluent French. She was such an interesting and generous lady. She left me a beautiful brooch in her will when she died. I treasure it to this day.

Angela and Roger had originally used their flat as a holiday home but decided to move in permanently because they loved the location and proximity to the sea so much. Angela and I became great friends; her daughter Alison was about my age and she used to visit her parents with her three children, Andrew, Nicholas and Holly.

Angela would pick apples from the large tree in her part of the garden and distribute them amongst her neighbours every autumn. There was a real sense of community spirit with everyone helping each other when and where we could. Angela would often babysit for us, or we would just pop into each other's houses for a cup of tea and a natter.

I loved to hear Angela play her piano. In the summer, we tended to have our windows wide open and the sound of her playing would rise into our sitting room along with the sound of rolling waves and the salty tang of the fresh sea air. It doesn't get much better than that.

Jemma and Lisa spent many happy summers playing with Angela and Roger's grandchildren. We would go to The Marine Hotel, which we could see from our sitting room and dining room windows, to swim in the outdoor pool. All in all, it was a very busy and happy time, but I was seriously thinking about one thing. Getting a proper job.

I had worked in a couple of local nursing homes, doing the odd shift here and there, and of course, the detested night duty to avoid the need for childcare.

The first nursing home I worked in was Astley House, situated on Dirleton Avenue. That was where I met Mags Gunn, now Carmichael, who joined the team shortly after I started working there. Coincidentally, Mags was from Thurso, but our paths had not crossed up there.

We found we had lots in common, especially a wicked, relentless and silly sense of humour. We became, and still are, the very best of friends. We have laughed and supported each other throughout far too many events and scrapes to mention here, from pretending to broadcast a cookery show to the nation from her kitchen, to steadfastly supporting each other through all of life's ups and downs, of which there were many. Suffice to say, she is my best friend and I do not know what I would do without her.

I became very fond of two sisters who resided in Astley House. Miss Hardy and Mrs. McCulloch. One day when we were discussing old coins, I mentioned that when I was a child I would keep any pennies with Queen Victoria on them rather than spend them in the tuck shop. I still have them.

It turned out that Miss Hardy had a small coin collection which she kept in an old Basildon Bond writing paper box, and she insisted that I should have it. I still take great pleasure in looking at those coins, and the two photographs they gave to me. One was of their mother dressed in the Edwardian clothes of the day, looking very elegant in her huge ornate hat, and one of the sisters as children with black buttoned up boots, pinafores and sun bonnets looking very angelic. Lovely gentle ladies, I will never forget them.

When I left Astley House, I became a bank nurse for Lothian Health Board. I was usually offered shifts in Roodlands General Hospital in Haddington, or in East Fortune Hospital.

I particularly enjoyed working in East Fortune. For one thing, it was very close to North Berwick and did not involve any major roads or traffic (yes, you've guessed, I still had difficulty with parking). East Fortune is another hospital with an interesting history. It began as a Royal Naval Airship Station at the beginning of the First World War. Two corrugated iron hangars were built to house the airships, with a third being constructed in 1917. The airships were two hundred metres long and forty-five metres high. They were used mainly for defence, soaring above the coastline looking for enemy submarines, and carrying out escort duties.

On the second of July 1919, at one forty-two a.m. Airship R.34, set off for the first direct flight from Britain to America. It must have been quite a spectacle that cold, misty morning. Someone managed to smuggle a kitten called Wopsie on board. Wopsie became the unofficial airship mascot. Also, on board were, twenty-two men, eight officers, two carrier pigeons and a stowaway (why do I feel like singing 'And a partridge in a pear tree'?)

In July 1921, the buildings were bought by the South-Eastern Counties of Scotland Joint Sanatorium Board. Most of the corrugated iron that was used in the construction of the airship hangars was salvaged and recycled to build a sanatorium.

In 1922, the first part of the sanitorium opened, and in 1925, it was opened fully, providing a possible one hundred and ninety-nine beds for long-term illness sufferers, chiefly, tuberculosis. It is worth remembering that antibiotics did not exist currently, so there was a genuine requirement for sanatoriums. Although Alexander Fleming discovered penicillin in 1929, its full potential was not reached until the early 1940s.

In 1939, at the start of World War Two, the hospital was utilised by the Emergency Medical Service (EMS) Scheme. The EMS was in place in various forms until the end of the war. It gave central government power over municipal and voluntary hospitals in the country. Patients in city hospitals were either discharged or evacuated to outlying areas in preparation for anticipated air-raid casualties. Four large wooden huts were built, three to be used as wards, the other to be used as an x-ray department and operating theatre. The Royal Air Force took possession of the hospital buildings in 1941, plus the airfield on the adjoining site.

Today the former airfield is the site used by the National Museum of Flight.

CHAPTER 12

TRANENT

"Choose a job you love, and you will never have to work a day in your life."
- Unknown

For the second time in my life, reading the local newspaper proved to be fortuitous for me. I read with interest that nearby Tranent Medical Centre was looking for a treatment room nurse. Twenty hours over five days per week.

I felt that I had the skills they were looking for but was seriously lacking in self-confidence. Could I do it? What about the school holidays? Who would look after the girls? What if one of them was ill one morning and couldn't go to school? I would need a car. If I didn't apply, I would always wonder if I could have got the job. I applied and was duly invited for an interview with Miss Carla Van Bunderen.

The day of my interview arrived. I was still a nervous driver and had an extraordinary fear of getting lost or breaking down. Before I could start to worry about the interview itself, I had the nerve-wracking job of finding the medical centre without getting lost and finding a place to park.

I found the town of Tranent easily enough. Tranent is a small town, close to the A1, about eleven miles east of Edinburgh. It was once an important mining town, and in fact, coal was first mined there in the 12th century. It is one of the oldest towns in East Lothian.

Being useless at map reading and with satellite navigation a long way off for the likes of me, I did something which usually worked for me when I was in danger of getting lost. I looked for an unsuspecting pedestrian and asked for directions. There he was, my knight in shining Tranent armour. I spied a small-looking man, wearing a bonnet and carrying a large, zipped shopping bag.

'Can you tell me how to get to Loch Square, please?' I called out to him.

'I am on my way there now, I have a doctor's appointment.' Result.

Then, quite out of character for me, I asked him if he wanted to hop in and accompany me whilst giving directions. He beamed, smiling from ear to ear. I could almost hear him relaying the story to his cronies and his wife, about the young woman who offered him a lift while she was on her way to an interview in the medical centre.

On arrival at the medical centre, we thanked each other and went our separate ways into the building. In spite of my nerves, I immediately felt at home there, and the easy banter with my new-found friend had relaxed me a bit.

The interview went well, and I suspect when I told Carla, who was shortly to become my line manager, that I had picked up a patient and brought him with me, it cinched the deal. It was just the kind of interaction between Tranent treatment room nurse and patients they had been hoping for, perhaps?

One of the first people to befriend me that April in 1991, was Felicia Justin, the Practice Nurse.

She explained that I had my own room, and that I should organise it any way I wanted to.

I was contracted to work four hours per day, and the rest of the time it would be used by the team of District Nurses and by the General Practitioners. I lost no time finding out where everything was kept and made a mental note to re-organise some of the cupboards and perhaps bring in some storage containers.

The District Nurses were a great bunch of people, extremely helpful and supportive. I was employed by Lothian Health board, as they were; Felicia was employed directly by the GPs.

There was also an amazing woman called Rena. She was a cross between a receptionist and lab technician. She knew where all stock and equipment were kept, how to re-order it or have it repaired. She was invaluable to me and to most of the doctors, I suspect.

The receptionists were very friendly, and I must say, we had many uproarious nights out, especially at Christmas. The GPs would also treat us to a night out at Christmas, which tended to be a bit more sedate, but only just.

Vi Ferguson was the practice manager at that time. I soon discovered that her two grandsons were at the same school as Jemma and Lisa, Law Primary in North Berwick. Andrew was in Jemma's class, and Donald was in Lisa's. I also knew her son and daughter-in-law who were pharmacists and owned a chemist shop in North Berwick. Small world indeed.

Vi had a wicked sense of humour, and we got on like a house on fire from the get-go.

I had a full list of patients every day. Mostly post-operative dressings, caring for venous and arterial ulcers, suture removal, blood tests, electrocardiograms (ECGs), ears to be syringed, and any walk-in minor injuries such as burns and scalds. I also assisted the GPs with minor operations such as the removal of ingrowing toenails, cysts etc.

One day, my telephone rang, and Martha on reception told me that there was a patient in the car park who was in labour.

To begin with, I thought it was a prank. Before starting my clinic that morning, we had been talking about a programme on television the night before. It was all about pregnancy and labour, and I had mentioned that I sometimes missed being a midwife.

I laughed and said something like, 'Nice try,' and hung up.

The phone rang again. Apparently, she was serious.

Still not totally convinced, I went down the corridor, past the now full waiting room, to reception. I looked through the glass doors towards the car park and there was indeed a mother in labour. She and her husband had been heading for the Eastern General Hospital in Edinburgh when they realised that they would not make it in time.

Time for action. We got a wheelchair and whisked the mum-to-be into my treatment room. The patients who were waiting to be seen by the GPs and by me looked on with interest and curiosity.

It had been seven years since I had delivered a baby. To be eligible to practice as a midwife you had to submit an Intention to Practice form to the Local Supervising Authority and have effective registration on the midwifery part of the Nursing and Midwifery Council register. At that time, I had neither.

It was decided, however, that it had been much longer than seven years since the GP I was with had delivered a baby, so while he would assist, I was the man for the job.

I don't think I have ever been so nervous. I tried to sound reassuring for Mum, but I was so far out of my comfort zone it was untrue.

We opened a stitch pack and I grabbed a pair of stitch scissors ready to cut the cord. We also opened a minor-op pack to get a pair of artery forceps to use as a cord clamp and asked the physiotherapy department to send along as many towels as they could spare for mopping and wrapping. If you had asked me to talk you through a delivery that morning, I really don't think I could have done it, but somehow, it all came flooding back to me and I was on some sort of midwifery auto-pilot.

A beautiful, healthy baby arrived in my treatment room soon after her parents had arrived in the car park. The GP took the towel swaddled baby, and with Mum and Dad's permission, took the sweet little bundle to the entrance of waiting room, where the patients had been waiting patiently whilst listening to Mum crying out in pain as only a woman in labour can, and me encouraging her to either push or breathe. I could hear the cheer from the patients when they saw the infant who had been the cause of all the commotion and disruption to clinics. I stayed with Mum awaiting the arrival of the placenta and keeping a close watch for any complications.

The story was in the local paper, maybe even some nationals, I can't remember. Shortly after the birth, the district midwives arrived, but they left again when they realised everything seemed to be well under control.

I was asked to escort Mum and baby in the ambulance to Edinburgh, so had to quickly call Mags who was now my trusty child minder as well as my best friend. I asked her if she was free to collect Jemma and Lisa from school and look after them until I returned, which thankfully she was. Imagine my dismay, but not surprise, when I was called in to be interviewed by someone in the midwifery hierarchy, who asked among other things, if I was aware that I had not submitted an Intention to Practice form that year. Apparently, on paper at least, it would have been better if the trained midwife had stood aside and let someone else deliver the baby on that occasion.

*

It was while I was working in Tranent that I discovered that Gran had pancreatic cancer. We were told she only had about six months to live. I think part of me refused to accept it. I subconsciously decided that if I ignored this information it would go away. I was devastated, and just could not imagine my life without Gran in it. She eventually had to go into a nursing home. When I first saw here there I thought that my heart might break. She looked so lost, so broken. We looked directly at each other and I started to speak, and she just shook her head and said, 'I know, I know.'

We didn't need words, we both knew that this was the worst possible thing that could have happened to her; her spark was gone, her independence was gone. I asked if Gran could come to stay with us for a week, for a wee holiday to spend time with her great-grandchildren and the nursing home agreed that it would do her good. Secretly I hoped it would go really well and that I might be able to move her out of the home and in with us.

Figure 20: *Gran, age 21*

It was more difficult than I could have imagined. She still smoked, her only vice and now pleasure, but I worried that she might get up in the night and set fire to herself and the house. As it happened, I awoke one night because I could smell a roast dinner being cooked. It was overwhelming – roast beef, potatoes, vegetables, the lot. I woke OH, but he couldn't smell anything and went back to sleep. The whole house was silent, but to me, the smell seemed to be getting stronger and stronger. It couldn't be my imagination. I got up and padded downstairs and into the empty kitchen. Nothing. Then I noticed that the electric kettle was sitting on the gas hob. As I approached it I heard the faint hissing of gas. Gran had got up to make herself some tea but had got mixed up, placing the electric kettle onto the gas hob. I turned the gas off with a heavy heart, and knew then, that with two little girls in the house I just could not risk having Gran living with us. She would have to go back to the nursing home.

Gran eventually became so ill that she was admitted to hospital. I got time off work to go and visit her. She had been unconscious for a few days, but she opened her eyes and we had what you might call a normal conversation about this and that. Again, my brain was playing tricks on me. I asked the nurse on duty how Gran was doing; she looked at me incredulously as if to say, 'You are joking, aren't you?' Gran died the next day. She had slipped back into unconsciousness shortly after I left, it was almost as if she had been waiting to say goodbye. I had lost my beloved grandmother, my confidante, my advisor and my best friend. I still think of her every day and especially on Jemma's birthday.

I thoroughly enjoyed working in Tranent but began to think I would like to spread my wings a bit and become a practice nurse. Felicia had whetted my appetite; practice nurses were required to carry out baby and travel vaccinations, run diabetic, asthma, and hypertension clinics, take cervical smears, run contraception and menopause clinics, and carry out new patient and elderly health checks to name but a few tasks and procedures.

Practice nursing was a relatively new concept, but numbers had grown immensely in the past ten years, and the wide range of skills required, highlighted the need for specific practice nurse training which was rapidly forthcoming, but at a financial cost to either the nurse or the practice she was employed by. Most practices looked at the training as an investment and were happy to provide it so long as it was justified.

As luck would have it, I found out that North Berwick Health Centre was looking for a part-time practice nurse. I couldn't believe it. The job I was after, right on my door step. I applied.

As I sat in one of consulting rooms being interviewed by various general practitioners (including my own GP), and the practice manager, my mind wandered back to the last time I had been sitting in that very room.

It was just after what became known in our family as the bathroom incident. Our washing machine had been moved upstairs, to what had once been the toilet, when the kitchen was renovated to allow room for a dishwasher. The tumble drier sat on top and it was a great arrangement. To help deaden the noise we had placed a piece of the new sitting room carpet (remember the paint incident?) underneath. The carpet did indeed deaden the noise, it also concealed the fact that the washing machine had sprung a leak. The carpet and the floor valiantly held on to the escaping water until the weight became too much to bear and the bathroom ceiling caved in. It had taken us about six months to painstakingly decorate the bathroom with its incredibly high ceiling. We had finally got our corner bath, two sinks each with a wall light above it, and even a bidet. It was my favourite room in the house so far. One evening I heard an almighty crash and rushed out into the hall to see where the noise had come from. Black dust was wafting from the bathroom. By this time OH was tentatively opening the door. We were horrified to see the washing machine protruding through the ceiling and that every receptacle, including the wall lights, was filled to brimming with ash deafening which was commonly used under the floorboards of Victorian dwellings as sound insulation. Our beautiful bathroom was now something akin to a bomb site. We closed the door on the carnage to be confronted with a reminder that this had once been room number thirteen.

This incident came shortly after Gran died. Jilly the dog had a hysterectomy and Jemma had her tonsils out. In short, it was the last straw. I felt totally overwhelmed and exhausted and soon found myself visiting my doctor in floods of tears rambling about ceilings and hysterectomies. Yes, you've guessed it, I was sitting in the self-same room having an interview for a job as a practice nurse.

By now, I was convinced that I was wasting my time and everyone else's, and relaxed a little, knowing that the interview was almost at an end. When it was over, I shook hands with everyone and thankfully left the room.

I was astounded and delighted when I received a telephone call later that day from one of the GPs telling me that the post was mine.

CHAPTER 13

NORTH BERWICK HEALTH CENTRE

"Luck is great, but most of life is hard work."

- Iain Duncan Smith

And so, it was, I found myself working in North Berwick Health Centre in June 1993. Norma McKay was the practice manager at that time, and she looked after an excellent team of reception and administrative staff.

There were two other practice nurses at that time, Moira and Joan, plus a treatment room nurse called Esme. We had the usual quota of district nurses and health visitors, a physiotherapy department and a chiropodist. Everyone was very friendly and helpful. I enjoyed friendly banter with Jackie, Issy, Mary, Joan and Elaine, the receptionists and the practice secretary Wendy.

The district nurses and health visitors were fantastic. Ann Richardson, who was a health visitor, became a good friend and was always available to bounce ideas off or to vent to. I soon found out that I shared a similar sense of humour with one district nurse in particular, Anne Chainey, who sadly, is no longer with us. Anne had a wicked sense of humour; the devilment was twinkling out of her eyes. When she became aware that I was game for a laugh we got into a few scrapes and one amazing venture, but more of that later.

One escapade involved a female GP celebrating her 40th birthday. Before her surgery started Anne and I went into her room and left a few surprises for her, including several KY jelly filled condoms strategically placed in cupboards and drawers. She told us later of her shock when she reached into her drawer for her stethoscope only to find her fingers around something strange and squidgy!

The health centre is attached by a small corridor to the Edington Cottage Hospital. The Edington opened in 1912 having been founded by Francis and Elizabeth Edington as a convalescent home for the people of North Berwick. When ownership was transferred to the National Health Service in 1948, it became a cottage hospital and it is still going strong today.

I was to find myself in the Edington as a patient one night. My back had gone into spasm big time. I couldn't even go to the toilet unassisted. I was admitted and given copious amounts of strong analgesia. As ever, the timing was less than perfect. Jemma was playing Cinderella in the towns annual pantomime, and OH and I had been invited to the 'Chow Italia Ball' in Edinburgh by our good friends Gennaro and Lorna. It was being held on a Sunday night because most of the people attending were restauranteurs, and Sunday was generally much quieter than a Friday or Saturday.

I am sure other patients thought my medication was a bit too potent when they heard me tearfully talking about Cinderella and wanting to go to the ball.

I managed to go to the pantomime in a borrowed wheelchair, and then, very foolishly, after I was discharged, I agreed to go to the ball courtesy of the painkillers which were making me a bit euphoric and rather senseless. I needed new shoes, so we called into John Lewis on the way to Gennaro and Lorna's. Mum and Dad were staying in Warrender to look after the girls. I tried on and bought the first pair I found; OH had to help me every step of the way, and the pain I was experiencing should have told me to go straight home.

Long story short, I spent the whole evening lying in a hotel bedroom surrounded by coats in great pain, feeling nauseated and miserable in-between dozing off under the influence of my analgesics. To make matters worse, the senior partner from the health centre had seen me in John Lewis, and was understandably not best pleased when of course, I was unfit for work on Monday.

*

The Scottish Refugee Council arranged for North Berwick to

become home for two separate groups of refugees from, what had formerly been the country of Yugoslavia. Bosnian refugees were housed in Cheylesmore Lodge, on Dirleton Avenue, between 1993 and 1995. Voluntary organisations helped to refurbish what had been an old people's home in the space of one weekend.

In 1999 Redcroft, situated in Ibris Place, which had also been an old people's residential home, housed fifty-nine Kosovan refugees, including fifteen children. The ultimate aim was to have the families living independently throughout Scotland.

I do not claim to fully comprehend what happened in Bosnia and Kosovo; the Encyclopaedia Britannica simply states:

Kosovo conflict, (1998-99) conflict in which ethnic Albanians opposed ethnic Serbs and the government of Yugoslavia (the rump of the former federal state, compromising the republics of Serbia and Montenegro in Kosovo. The conflict gained widespread international attention and was resolved with the intervention of the North Atlantic Treaty Organization (NATO)

From what I can understand (and I apologise if it is not wholly factual), after the death of Yugoslavian President Josip Broz (also known as President Tito), in 1980, Yugoslavia started to unravel at the seams. Throughout the 1980s, communist authorities in Kosovo, Serbia and Yugoslavia acknowledged that interethnic affairs had reached a critical state but refused to allow public debate. Slobodan Milosevic, 'the butcher of the Balkans', appeared on the scene in 1987. He became President of Yugoslavia in 1997.

Conflicts based upon ethnicity raged from 1992 until 1995. Deaths in Srebrenica were the highest mass killings since World War Two. Srebrenica literally became a concentration camp.

Through my work as a practice nurse I became involved in the care and welfare of the remarkable people, especially the women and children living in Redcroft, and was to discover, first hand, facts about their lives which appalled and horrified me. I found it astounding and shocking that atrocities such as they had been subjected to had been happening in a country which was only about a three-hour flight from where I was living and working. I felt deeply saddened and troubled and wanted to do something more other than what was required through work.

I spoke to Anne Chainey who was actively involved in collecting toys and other useful items to take to Redcroft, and we agreed to put out feelers and find out if there was anything we could do. We decided that a day out in Edinburgh for the ladies would be a good start. I happened to mention our plight to a friend of mine, Patricia Sheridan, in the Nether Abbey one night over a glass of wine (I got to know Patsy after her Great Dane, Ruby, became stranded on a rock in the sea and we had to call out the Coastguard, but that is a different story altogether). I had met Patsy's cousin Alison Craig a couple of times. Alison had a regular radio show on Radio Forth at that time (she is now an author, broadcaster and reporter for 'The One Show') and she had some useful and valuable contacts. I was invited to Alison's for dinner and there we discussed what we could do. Her husband David Scott owned and ran a chain of restaurants called Howies and he was more than happy to invite all of the women for a meal in one of his restaurants after a day of sightseeing. After that, the plan snowballed. Thanks to Alison and Patsy we had a whole host of places to visit and goodies for the women of Redcroft. I was interviewed on Radio Forth but felt quite foolish in that I couldn't really answer most of the questions because of confidentiality issues, but word got out that we had a big day planned.

Anne, Patsy and I arranged to meet with all the ladies at North Berwick train station. I had had a cold and subsequently lost my voice which didn't help matters. We had arranged for taxis to pick us up when we arrived at Waverley Station in Edinburgh, completely free of charge, to take us around the city. When we arrived, I spotted a people carrier with its door wide open; the driver seemed to be looking at me and I reckoned it was one of the taxis. I climbed in but couldn't say much because of my voice. I was duly followed by several of the Kosovan women. The driver of the vehicle was rather startled and explained that she was not a taxi but was simply waiting for a relative. By now I had several women behind me, so I decided to exit via the other door, again duly followed but my entourage. We piled out onto the pavement on the opposite side of the car. What with the obvious language difficulties between us, and the fact that I couldn't speak at all I never did manage to explain what had just happened. I often wonder what they thought of it.

We took an open top bus tour of the city courtesy of the bus company, had lunch, and then went on for afternoon tea courtesy of Jenner's and every woman in the group was given a hamper full of Jenner's delights. At the end of an amazing day, we made our way to Howies and it was time to relax and let our hair down. There were more gifts to hand out including some lovely underwear from La Senza in Princes Street, and bags containing cosmetics. The look of wonder and gratitude on the faces of these women who had been through and witnessed so much including rape and torture will remain with me forever. Let's just say there were lots of tears.

Howies kept the wine flowing and presented us with a sumptuous meal. We were all in high spirits in more ways than one and had a blissful evening before making our way back to North Berwick. That train journey is one I shall never forget. One old lady started to sing a Yugoslavian folk song. One by one all the other women joined in, eyes moist with tears. It was heart-rending and is one of my most cherished memories.

Figure 21: *North Berwick Health Centre staff. Self, standing back row, right.*

We had known Jilly was half working collie, but we had no idea what the other half was. Lots of people asked if she was a flat-coat retriever, and she did have a distinct similarity to that breed although she was much smaller. After her hysterectomy, she did not recover well, and we found out she had cancer. We were devastated and heartbroken. I thought about getting another dog, but OH was not so keen.

Yet again, the East Lothian Courier came up trumps, there it was… 'Flat Coat Cross puppies for sale'.

Surely this was meant to be? After a bit of a discussion about the pros and cons of getting another dog, we arranged to go and look at the puppies the following weekend. Just for a look, mind you. The girls were ecstatic when they saw the pups. They were all black, with great big puppy dog eyes, and totally adorable. It was a done deal, and my poor OH was completely outnumbered.

We had decided that we wanted another bitch, but by the time we got there, there were only two dogs left. Lisa picked up the smallest and most subdued puppy and announced, 'This is the one.' We had ourselves a little boy. We had to wait until the puppies had been weaned of course before we could take him home, but this gave us time to puppy-proof the house and garden. That said, it was pretty safe by that time given Lisa's tendency to be overly adventurous and a bit accident prone.

When Jemma was a toddler, she amused herself with books and toys when I was busy. The house in Thurso, being of standard size, had baby-proof everything courtesy of Mothercare. Generally, if I left Jemma playing while I left the room, she was in the same spot, more or less, when I returned, apart from the time I thought I had lost her only to find her fast asleep in her little Parker-Knoll rocking chair Mum and Dad had bought for her.

None of the safety gadgets we had purchased for Jemma fitted the new house. The sockets were the old round pinned plug ones before it was rewired. The stairs were much too wide for shop-bought baby gates. Lisa loved to climb door frames and generally get into everything she could. A favourite pastime was trying to stick screwdrivers into the round electrical sockets. She managed to tip a bowl full of setting table jelly all over the bare kitchen floor. The jelly promptly settled into every crevice and space between the floor boards and could still be there for all I know, I certainly couldn't remove it. We had a large wraparound fireguard for the now gas fire in the sitting room, and another wraparound fireguard surrounding all the tools required for renovations which were being kept in the dining room at that time.

It was much the same when they were babies; Jemma sat like a little doll in her coach-built pram with her pristine white broderie anglaise cover. Hat, be it woolly or frilly on her head, toys within reach. Lisa usually yanked her hat off, threw the toys and cover out of the pram and hung over the hood (well strapped in, I hasten to add) looking at where she had been rather than where she was going. Oh happy, happy days.

With great excitement we collected Bracken on the first day of the school summer holidays, which was of course ideal timing. I had taken a week off work too just to make sure he settled in. Jilly who was ten, bless her, was obviously not feeling too well and could not have seen the new puppy far enough. She chose to lie as far away from him as possible. Bracken, on the other hand, had other ideas. He was missing his mum, and Jilly was the next best thing.

Bracken was an extremely pampered pooch with three besotted females anticipating his every need and whim. I got up early to warm milk to mix with Farley's baby rusks, or to make him scrambled eggs most mornings. When he cried at night, I paced around with him slung over my shoulder just like a baby. Jemma and Lisa hated to hear him whine pitifully and got very upset; although Jemma usually managed to fall asleep again, Lisa did not.

The plan was to start as we meant to carry on, in that he was not going to be allowed upstairs at night. He had a substantial bed in the kitchen. At bedtime, I would wrap an alarm clock in a blanket and place it beside him, which was supposed to sound like his mother's heartbeat, and a baby hot water bottle to offer comfort and warmth like he had from his brothers and sisters. Night after night he howled and whimpered like his little heart was breaking. By now, I was feeling sleep deprived and knew I had to go back to work soon, and so, one fateful night, I fetched him from the kitchen, took him upstairs and placed him on the bed beside me. He went out like a light and did not utter a sound until he needed to wee in the morning. He whimpered to let me know nature was calling; I picked him up, placed him onto the newspaper I had thought to bring upstairs with me. He did his business neatly and without fuss on the paper. He turned back towards the bed and looked longingly at it. There was no going back now.

He was a fussy eater and would not eat his Pedigree Chum puppy food. Why would he when he could have scrambled eggs and rusks? I started going to Struth's the butchers to buy cheap cuts of meat (much to Mr. Struth's amazement) and eventually frozen dog food which consisted mostly of minced-up offal. The rather gloopy mixture was bright red in colour as it defrosted in the large tray I kept for that purpose.

One day, Jemma came into the kitchen just as the mound of offal was ready to be cooked. She looked at it with disgust and said, 'What is that? It looks horrible.'

'Dog mince,' I replied.

Jemma then shrieked and tearfully announced that there was no way she could or would eat minced-up dog.

This reminds me of another incident. I was driving Jemma and Lisa home from school, preoccupied by the vast number of cars involved in the daily school run and little unpredictable pedestrians.

'Do we have mince?' came a little voice from the back of the car.

'I really don't know, I haven't thought about dinner yet,' I replied, concentrating on the road.

'No, do WE have mince,' came the slightly impatient reply.

I repeated that I had not had time to think about dinner but told them that there could well be some mince in the freezer if that was what they wanted.

With an exasperated sigh Jemma then said, 'No, I mean do humans have mince? We have liver, kidneys, heart, so do we have mince?'

I seem to remember she decided to become a vegetarian shortly after that.

Sadly, the tragic day we had been dreading came along. The vet said he could do no more for Jilly, and that euthanasia was the only way forward. It was a Monday, I will never forget it. I walked back home with tears streaming down my face. I had explained to the vet that Jemma had gone on holiday with a school friend and her family. They were due to return on Friday. I asked if we could possibly delay putting Jilly to sleep until Saturday morning, and the vet said we could, that another few days would not be detrimental to her. We agreed a time for him to come to the house. It was like living under a huge, black, all-consuming cloud.

Saturday came; the girls were inconsolable. We had decided to bury Jilly in the garden. OH, who was also heartbroken, had used grave digging as therapy of sorts; he could have buried a couple of full-grown men in the hole he dug. I still have an old lemonade bottle that he dug up, it is from John Macintyre's aerated water factory which was on Forth Street Lane in North Berwick. The factory may have been opened to coincide with the temperance movement (which began in the 1880s, encouraging people not to drink alcohol, use tobacco, play sports or use strong language on a Sunday – those were the days), but I have not been able to find out much about it. Watch this space.

It was so hard to accept what was about to happen. Jilly was still enjoying her walks to the beach and her food, but in our hearts, we knew it was the kindest thing we could do for her. OH stayed with the girls in the dining room, I was with Jilly and the vet in the sitting room. Jilly lay down in one of the turret bays. Her breathing had become laboured, and her eyes looked dull and glassy. Lying on her side the swelling on her abdomen was more obvious. I lay on the floor beside her, stroking her head and gazing into her eyes, talking softly to her and telling her what a good girl she was, as she drifted off into her final pain-free sleep.

OH and the vet carried her out into the garden wrapped in a pure white sheet. They gently placed her into the huge hole in the ground. The vet had advised taking Bracken out with us so that he could see what was happening to Jilly. He explained that he might be unsettled if she just vanished. When we got into the garden, Bracken headed straight for the mound of earth waiting to cover the white sheet containing our beloved girl. He climbed up on top and proceeded to dig; his nose and extremely large paws were covered with brown soil as he gleefully scuffled around totally oblivious to the solemnity of the situation. I didn't know whether to laugh or get angry with him, so I just kept right on crying.

Figure 22: *Dad with from left to right, Jilly, Bracken and Dad's dog Rex*

Figure 23: *Bracken*

When I first started to work at NBHC, I spent two weeks in clinic, and then two weeks visiting patients in their own homes. More often than not, when I finished work, my car would just kind of steer itself to Mags. We would drink tea and offload, gossip, sometimes cry but mostly laugh. Mags and Bill had two children by that time, Lyndsey and Lewis. Jemma and Lisa loved being with Mags too and found it no hardship to be looked after by her when I was at work. She was the perfect child minder, and I will be eternally grateful to her for being just like another mum for my girls.

We would bake, exercise, talk, listen, sing, confide, understand, reassure, and generally support each other through thick and thin. We gained strength from each other, still do. Lyndsey learned to walk in our house, Lewis had one of his socks swallowed by Bracken. I'd like to see any dog try that these days; Lewis is now six foot seven and plays rugby for Edinburgh and Scotland. Mags got ready for her wedding to Bill in Warrender. I could go on and on. Suffice to say Mags never fails to lift my spirits. She is genuine, loving, and always there for me. I feel so proud to be able to call her my best friend.

Figure 24: *Mags and me, 1999*

CHAPTER 14

WITCHES AND WATER THERAPY

"Double, double toil and trouble; Fire burn, and cauldron bubble."
- William Shakespeare, from Macbeth

As I have already mentioned, North Berwick had more than its fair share of very large, imposing houses, and I felt fortunate to be able to see inside many of them while I was out and about visiting patients.

Most were like Warrender in that they had been divided into flats, but a few remained intact, complete with original servant call bells, and other original features including a speaking tube, or voice pipe which had been used as a communication system within the house. The following may give you a better idea about North Berwick in days gone by:

A quote from a publication in 1902 reads:

'Each year adds to the number and graciousness of the stately villas of the west end'

Another from 1903 reads:

'It was remarked on the Links this week that at one moment there were in the course of play, The Prime Minister, the Speaker of the House of Commons, four members of parliament, two Bishops of the Church of England, three eminent

professors, a field marshal, two generals and a famous Tibetan explorer.'

And in 1902 it was reported that:

'The King is staying at the residence of the Prince and Princess of Saxe-Weimar. While His Majesty was at dinner, The North Berwick Pipe Band played outside.'

North Berwick had gained popularity as a holiday destination after the Prince of Wales paid a visit in 1859, and again in 1902 when he was King. The advertising slogan 'Biarritz of the North' was created in 1889. Notable families and 'The Cream of London's Society' descended on North Berwick to enjoy the fresh salty sea air, sandy beaches, harbour and golf courses. In August and September, they would take up residence in their holiday homes, most of which had been built in York Road and Cromwell Road (which collectively was known as Millionaire's Row by locals) with armies of nannies, butlers, housekeepers and footmen bringing valued trade to the town as the local grocers, tradesmen and merchants catered to their needs and requirements.

Among these notable families were Robert Chamber the publisher, the Astor family, Alexander, Isabella and Barbara Keiller of Dundee (marmalade and jam manufacturers), Lord Advocate for Scotland and the Prime Minister, Arthur James Balfour.

During the 1860s, the family of Thomas Stevenson, lighthouse engineer, would holiday in Anchor Villa in West-Bay Road, as did his son and grandson, author, Robert Louis Stevenson. It is understood that the island of Fidra inspired the book *Treasure Island,* and *Catriona,* the sequel to *Kidnapped.* Any one of the islands visible from the North Berwick coastline, including Craigleith and Lamb, not forgetting the imposing Bass Rock with the ruined covenanters' prison could easily inspire an author or poet to write about them.

Another famous piece of literature said to be inspired by North Berwick is *Tam O'Shanter* by Robert Burns.

"Coffins stood round, like open presses, that shaw'd the dead in their last dresses: And by some devilish cantraip slight, each in its cauld hand held a light."

There has been a historic connection with North Berwick and witchcraft for hundreds of years.

James VI of Scotland, the son of Mary Queen of Scots, became James I, King of England and Ireland from the union of the Scottish and English crowns on the 24th of March 1603. Until that union the kingdoms of Scotland and England were individual self-governing states with their own judiciaries, parliaments and laws.

A bride was chosen for James to safeguard the new monarchy's survival. Fourteen-year-old Anne of Denmark. Some accounts say that James had to seek refuge off the coast of Norway en route to meet his new bride when his ship was nearly shipwrecked in a violent storm. Others say that it was Anne who sought refuge in Norway whilst encountering the violent storms. Either way, violent storms were involved and caused James to have a re-think about witchcraft!

Seemingly Anne's ship had been forced to seek shelter off the coast of Norway by fierce storms. On hearing this, James gallantly and some say romantically, set sail from Leith with a 300-strong entourage to fetch her. The couple were duly married in Oslo before returning to Scotland. The newlyweds sailed from Denmark to Scotland on the first of May 1590. The fleet of ships once more encountered violent and dangerous weather, but it was noted by some that the King's ship was abused and lashed by the sea more than any other ship. The admiral of the Danish fleet promptly blamed witchcraft as a cause for the storms. Up until this experience James had been quite lenient towards witchcraft but these events changed his views on the subject and he began his persecution of witchcraft in Scotland. He wrote a book called *Daemonologie* which instructed his supporters and followers to prosecute and condemn anyone thought to be involved with witchcraft. On his return to Scotland, James attended the North Berwick witch trials which ran from 1590 to 1592. At least seventy so-called witches, some of whom were nobles of the Scottish court, were accused of holding covens on the Auld Kirk Green in North Berwick.

A Tranent maidservant called Geilie Duncan was interrogated after arousing suspicion of witchcraft by displaying 'miraculous healing ability'. Geilie vehemently denied any association to witchcraft and the devil but following prolonged and relentless torture and the discovery of a so-called 'devil's mark' on her neck, she confessed to being a witch and admitted to being at a meeting in North Berwick on Halloween 1590 with over two hundred other witches, where the plot against the King was hatched with the devil presiding over the proceedings. She was tortured yet again until she named her accomplices which included Doctor John Fian, a local school master, who was accused of being a coven leader, and a woman called Agnes Sampson who was a respected midwife and healer within the community. Each person named by Geilie, was brought before the King and many confessed, while being tortured, to meeting the devil in North Berwick Kirk yard and devoting themselves to him by plotting to poison the King and his family and to sink his ship. Some confessions even claimed that on Halloween 1590, the witches were instructed by the devil to dig up corpses buried in the Kirk graveyard and to remove various joints and organs which were attached to a dead cat and thrown into the sea to create the storm which had nearly shipwrecked the King's ship. The confessions extracted during torture, were suspiciously familiar in detail.

Poor Agnes Sampson was thought to be examined by the King himself in Holyrood Palace. Accounts tell of her being attached to her cell wall by an instrument called a 'witches' bridle' which had four sharp prongs which were forced into the mouth against the cheeks and tongue. She was not allowed to sleep, although how she could possibly sleep with that contraption torturing her the devil only knows! Eventually Agnes confessed to fifty-three charges against her. She was strangled and burned as a witch.

Dr Fian was brutally crippled by torture. The rack was used, stretching and dislocating his joints. He had needles inserted into his fingernails before they were ripped out.

Geilie was hanged as a witch in 1591.

Today we can only estimate that between 3,000 and 4,000 people accused as witches were executed in Scotland between 1560 and 1707

*

The arrival of the railway line to North Berwick in 1850 not only boosted tourism, it boosted trade. Many new hotels were built to cater for the influx of people keen to enjoy all the pleasures and pastimes North Berwick had to offer.

When the Marine Hotel was built in 1875, an access road was required so Cromwell Road was created. It was fashionable for the gentry to book into the Marine Hotel for hydropathic remedies. Sea-water bathing was encouraged by Victorian doctors and was thought to be therapeutic. Local children were often paid to fetch buckets of sea water for those unable to gain access to the beach by themselves. The hotel could offer guests salt and freshwater baths. Water was piped to the hotel from the sea and stored in large tanks. Fresh water came from a well in the grounds. The hotel also proffered putting greens designed by local golfer Ben Sayers and a bowling green. Ben Sayers was born in Leith, but he later moved to North Berwick where he opened a golf club manufacturing factory and patented several innovative club designs. He was also involved with the early manufacture of gutta-perch golf balls or 'gutties' as they were affectionately known. He was an excellent golf instructor and could pride himself in saying that he had taught George, Prince of Wales, later to become King George the fifth, and Her Majesty Queen Alexandra amongst other dignities and royals, to play golf.

*

As well as being one of the North Berwick Practice Nurses, I was actively involved with St Andrew Blackadder Church. I was on the congregational board and sang in the choir. Much to my delight I even got to climb up the bell tower and ring the bell one Sunday evening thanks to a lovely man called Jim. When I joined the church, it was simply St Andrews, but in 1989 it amalgamated with another North Berwick church, Blackadder.

St Andrew Blackadder church held a youth club on a Friday night, and I would often help out. When they had a disco, I would rope Mags into helping out too. We had great fun, probably more than the kids did. Lisa attended these discos on a regular basis and she would try hard to pretend that she didn't know me.

St Andrew Blackadder, as a building, was beginning to feel a bit inadequate for the congregation. In short, we were running out of space. The building was not suitable for modern-day requirements, and so, in 1999, the Kirk Session presented 'The New Century Challenge'. This involved extension and improvement of the church. The floor was raised to the level of the original galleries and became the new Sanctuary. The new ground floor became a suite of meeting rooms and a new chapel was created.

It must be mentioned here that the cost of the work, which was completed in December 2000, was met by the congregation, and a loan from central church funds. The new interior serves the community very well, and the sanctuary is also used as a venue for 'Fringe by The Sea' series of summer concerts, but I am getting ahead of myself.

Figure 25: *St Andrew Blackadder Church Choir*

I was involved with the fundraising, which meant visiting church members in their own homes, showing them the plans and explaining how we hoped to raise funds to complete the work.

One event really sticks in my mind. A ceilidh was organised, which was to be held in Tantallon Castle.

The castle sits on cliffs looking out towards the Bass Rock. It is a popular tourist attraction and has been used in pop videos in the past. On occasion, it is closed to the public because of adverse weather conditions, so it was a bit of a concern wondering how this historic venue would work out. We needn't have worried. The evening was perfect. The Nether Abbey Hotel provided us with a bar, there were barbeques cooking up the only storm of the night, and there was dancing in the Great Hall of the castle for the first time in hundreds of years. An unforgettable evening stamped on my memory forever and all for an excellent cause.

Another truly memorable day was spent with members of the church choir in St Mary's Collegiate Church in Haddington. The church, the building of which started in 1380, has magnificent interior vaulting and excellent acoustics. It has been used by the BBC many times for television and radio production, but on that frosty November day, we worked hard to record a compilation of hymns, carols and songs. (We actually did this twice while I was in the choir, once as a cassette tape, then as a compact disc.) Our Musical Director, Philip Boon, had even composed several pieces, and our Minister, Eddie McKenna, had a solo. The sales of the CD helped with the fundraising efforts. We arrived in St Mary's early one frosty Saturday morning and sang our hearts out well into the evening. Everyone had brought food varying from sandwiches and sausage rolls and quiche to salads, chilli and lasagne. There was lots of home baking and fruit, and naturally, copious amounts of tea and coffee consumed. It was extremely tiring, but I would not have missed that magical Christmassy day for the world. I think my copy of the CD got left in America so if anyone out there can help me out?

I also became involved with the Girl Guides. Jemma had joined, and at the parents' evening it was announced that the unit would fold if no one would volunteer to help the Unit Leader. Before I could stop myself, my hand was in the air, and so I found myself becoming Assistant Leader in training, buying my uniform and going on various courses. This is what I signed myself up for:

As an Assistant Leader, you will work with others in the team to make the most of the skills and time you are able to give. Provide a safe girl-only space where girls and young women can discover their full potential and encourage them to be a powerful force for good.

Provide ongoing leadership and support to members of the unit.

Take an active role in creating and delivering an accessible and inclusive programme, based on the Girl guiding programme for your section.

Encourage and support the members of the unit in making decisions within the unit and the wider Girl guiding community.

Keep up to date with new resources and programme initiatives and use them as appropriate. Complete relevant training for the role, keeping your skills up to date. Comply with current Girl guiding policies and regulations.

Maintain clear communication with parents and carers and gain all necessary permissions for activities.

Support the Unit Leader to ensure all activity instructors/visitors to the unit meet the requirements as laid out in The Guiding Manual.

Provide an initial response to any concerns or complaints from girls and young women or their parents/carers, following the Girl guiding Safeguarding Policy and escalating issues to the Unit Leader if appropriate.

In real terms, it meant preparing for the weekly guide meetings, coming up with ideas, old and new, to present each week. Organising outings and parties. Arranging fundraising events and activities. I found myself spending weekends at Alison Cargill House in Haddington with twenty-plus Guides or Brownies enjoying assorted outdoor activities and sing-songs.

It was great fun, helping the girls with their individual challenges as they worked towards innumerable badges and consequently, personal development.

I helped to organise a series of first aid meetings. I enlisted work colleagues, the local ambulance service and the Red Cross.

The girls were allowed into the ambulance which parked outside the school hall where our meetings were held. They got to try cardiopulmonary resuscitation, and various types of bandaging. The next day, I received several telephone calls from mothers who wanted to thank me. Apparently, some of the girls were very enthusiastic about the meeting and raved about it when they got home. That was very rewarding indeed At least one became a doctor, but I am sure I cannot claim any credit for that.

I flourished with all my new-found activities and skills, but it was quite tiring, and took its toll, especially with my unpredictable spinal column, and dicey discs. It also meant that I couldn't nip out to the shops or along the High Street if I was in a hurry. Without fail, I would run into patients, parents of Girl Guides, or fellow choir members. They usually wanted to stop and talk, ask questions, or just pass the time of day. Little did I realise how much I would miss that contact when we moved to America in 2000.

CHAPTER 15

GRAN, PAPA, SAWNEY BEAN

AND PSYCHICS

"More than anything else, this new century demands new thinking; We must change our materially based analyses of the world around us to include broader, more multidimensional perspectives."

- Albert Einstein

"There are more things in Heaven and Earth, Horatio, than are dreamt of in your philosophy."

- William Shakespeare, Hamlet

After Papa died, my gran used to come and spend up to a month at a time staying with us in North Berwick. Gran and I were kindred spirits and were just as comfortable sitting silently in a room together as we were when laughing and joking. As I have mentioned, Jemma was born on Gran's birthday, and Lisa was born on my papa's birthday which seemed to create a special bond between them.

Gran had worked as a domestic servant when she left school aged fourteen, so the fact that the staircase in Warrender was too big for my vacuum cleaner to reach all the way to the top or indeed the bottom, did not phase her, likewise with the lack of a window cleaner. She had been there and done that and proved to be more than up to those challenges. I must add, she provided me with solutions, not physical labour, although she would have done given half a chance; she was a bit of a daredevil, was my gran.

Gran also had a propensity to all things psychic and spiritual. I vividly remember one instance when Jemma was a baby. Jemma had been distressed and seemed to be in pain. We managed to get through the night with Calpol and cuddles until the morning when I called the surgery and got an appointment to see our GP. Just after we had got home from the doctors armed with antibiotics, the telephone rang. It was Gran asking how Jemma was. I went into a spiel about what the doctor had said, when it dawned on me: *How does Gran know Jemma has been ill?*

When I questioned her about it, she simply said she just knew that Jemma had had a bad night.

Gran would often ask me to promise that I would go and visit a medium when she was, as she so eloquently put it, 'kicking up the daisies' and that she would contact me and prove that there is indeed life after death. I would dismiss the idea, usually with a sigh of, 'Oh, Gran,' and change the subject.

In the early 70s, my grandparents moved from 35 Woodbank Road Crosshouse to 65 Gatehead Road, right across the road from our house at number 26. I was delighted, but I suspect my mother was not quite so enamoured.

Over the years I would often pop across in the evenings just to visit and chat, watch TV or play card games. Gran and Papa had a colour TV before we did. I loved watching Upstairs Downstairs. Gran enjoyed game shows, and the popular American detective series which were in abundance at that time. Papa enjoyed watching Tommy Cooper, Songs of Praise and the news, but would often go to bed early to tune in from the comfort of his bed (a trait I have inherited). I remember he had a bright orange, round television, which could be hung from a chain secured to the ceiling, although he kept it on the stand it came with, by his bedside table. It looked a bit like a space helmet. Don't you just love the 70s?

When I got married and moved to Thurso, I missed Gran terribly; we would phone and write regularly. What I would have given for email, WhatsApp and Skype at that time. I can still remember Gran and Papa's telephone number, and can almost hear Gran's telephone voice as she answered saying, 'Hello, this is Kilmarnock double-two-six-oh-two.'

When Jemma was born on Gran's 70th Birthday, Gran was ecstatic. When Lisa was born on my papa's birthday, we were all a bit incredulous. Sadly, Papa was in hospital by then suffering from what was known as pre-senile dementia. It was unbelievably sad to see him hold baby Lisa and not acknowledge it. He would have told the world and his mother about his great-granddaughter being born on his birthday had he been well. He was such a big softie. When I was small, he would take me and my cousins out for a 'run' in the car on a Sunday. This often meant that he would stop at a local pub for a quick pint after he had sent out bottles of cola and bags of crisps for us.

Children (and sometimes women) were not allowed in pubs at that time and let's not even mention the drinking and driving which was acceptable.

Papa was Transport Manager at Scottish Aviation Limited, (SAL) in Prestwick. His office was attached to a large hangar and it smelled of petrol and engines. Two seats in the office were leather aircraft chairs, and I loved to sit on them and pretend to be on a flight to somewhere exotic. Sometimes I was taken to the telephone exchange where a delightful lady called Margaret Anderson worked. I seem to remember that she wore bright orange lipstick (as did her sister, I suspected that they shared the tube.) At that time connections between phones at SAL were made manually using junction boxes, plugs and sockets. Margaret would let me sit on one of the empty seats with headphones that were much too big for me, on my head. I would push the plugs attached to cords into the sockets on the board in front of me, not live of course, and pretend to be Margaret's assistant. There was always a ticking noise in the telephone exchange. I remember asking what it was and being told not to worry about it unless it stopped. I now know that, due to the Cold War, it was an early warning system in case of a nuclear attack.

I grew up around aeroplanes and would often get to see them up close and personal. The back of Papa's office was the perfect place to watch the annual air show held at Prestwick Airport. Dad worked at SAL too, and I liked nothing better than to visit where he and Papa worked.

I felt strangely important and scared in equal measure if Papa got annoyed with one of his employees, especially on the telephone. He would turn into a sort of raging bull (well, he was a Taurus, I suppose). I thought the transformation in my lovely gentle Papa was incredible and was glad that I never caused him to behave like that.

As I mentioned, Gran and Papa had a static caravan in New England Bay caravan site. It was situated in Luce Bay, Port Logan, near Stranraer. They would go down most weekends and I often went with them. Papa's sister, Auntie Agnes, would accompany them sometimes, as well as her daughter Nanette and her husband Tony. Papa loved to catch up with his relatives, and it was a real home from home. Gran used the caravan toilet and shower room as a pantry. The caravan was brand new when they bought it, the toilet had never been used for its intended purpose, so it is not quite as bad as it sounds. She felt it was much more hygienic to use the shower and toilet facilities provided by what was a very quiet site at that time, and that pantry space was paramount. No shop, no bar, just a toilet and shower block although I believe it is very different now.

Their caravan was right on the edge of the beach; you stepped out of the caravan door, walked over some pebbles and stones, and there it was, sandy beach and rolling waves. On a clear day, you could see the basking sharks' dorsal fins in the distance as they fed on zooplankton (with their metre-wide mouths.)

Papa's cousin, Tammy, was a dairyman on a farm. I loved to visit the byre (cowshed) and watch the cows being milked. I never did grow to appreciate the distinct farmyard aroma. His wife, Netta, without fail, had fresh baked bread and scones in their cottage kitchen, and there was always a big jug of creamy milk and copious amounts of butter and home-made jam and marmalade on the table.

The drive down the west coast of Scotland to the caravan was interesting. Ailsa Craig, an extinct volcano and uninhabited island from which blue honed granite has been quarried for many years to make curling stones, can be seen protruding impressively from the sea for most of the journey. Further along the coast road we passed the area where there is an infamous cave, locally known to have been where a rather nasty man by all accounts, called Sawney (Alexander) Bean had lived with 'Black Agnes Douglas' his common-law wife.

As the story goes, Sawney, who had been born in East Lothian, the son of a hedger and ditch-digger, moved to South Ayrshire and set up home with Agnes. Bean did not relish a future labouring like his father, and so he and the likeminded Agnes supposedly made a living by ambushing unsuspecting travellers, murdering and robbing them. Not content with that, afterwards they would drag the bodies back to the cave where they would disjoint them and eat the flesh. What a lovely couple.

Papa loved to tell this cannibalistic tale and would slow down as he drove past for dramatic effect. I was never sure whether I wanted to look or not. In fact, the cave cannot be seen from the road, but I didn't know that at the time. It is about 150 feet below the hilltop which has a car park on it now, and it is thought to run about a mile deep into the hillside. Allegedly, Sawney and his incestuous family lived in the cave for about twenty-five years before they were discovered. Body parts were found on neighbouring beaches and locals noted that some people had disappeared. One evening some fairgoers witnessed a murder and a search party was organised to seek out the evil culprit, allegedly led by King James VI of Scotland. Once captured, and after body parts had been found hanging to dry or being pickled in the cave, Sawney and his family were taken to the Tollbooth in Edinburgh to be executed. The women and children were burned at the stake, the men were dismembered and left to bleed to death.

A macabre tale which, be it truth or fiction, captivated and horrified us as children and triggered many a nightmare in the caravan further down that very road.

Papa came with me when I went to sit my driving test. Nobody thought I would pass, least of all my husband-to-be. If truth be told, I didn't really expect to pass it either. I had never taken an official lesson. Dad taught me to drive, and he could often be seen mopping sweat from his brow from the ever-present duster in his glove compartment. Once an army man, always an army man, he had a place for everything and liked it to be kept that way, preferably without dust.

About halfway through the test, certain that I had made a major mistake, I relaxed, resigning myself to a re-sit. When we returned to the test centre, there was no sign of Papa, but there was a fire engine in the car park positioned in such a way which would make my exit a bit difficult unless I reversed into a space between two cars, not really my thing as you know, but hey, needs must. I had to get back to college as quickly as possible for an important lecture, so I reversed into the space, expertly, even though I say so myself. I passed the test. Bounding out of the car with the pink slip in my hand, I set off to look for Papa. He loved looking in butcher shop windows and that is exactly where I found him.

'I passed!' I shrieked.

'Oh, I think ah ken,' he replied nonchalantly. He barely looked away from the window full of red meat, but I knew he had been watching the whole time.

Gran and Papa would visit for a couple of weeks at a time when I got married and moved to Thurso. This was when I first noticed Papa had begun to exhibit some strange traits and become extremely emotional. It was the onset of dementia, but no one would recognise it for quite some time. It was so sad to see that once raging bull become lost and alone-looking. He was eventually taken to hospital not long before Lisa was born. I hated seeing him in there, the whole family did, but Dad took it very badly and never missed an opportunity to go and see his father. He would usually come home from work, collect Gran and then travel back to Ayr to visit. I vowed that I would do the same for Dad if he found himself in a similar situation. Thankfully at the time of writing this he is a picture of health, but it is a promise I intend to keep.

Gran would often mention times she had been to a Spiritualist Church, and messages she had received. She went to Crosshouse Parish Church regularly too, in fact we often went together before I got married, then we would come home to a steaming hot bowl of Papa's homemade soup. He loved making soup and I have yet to taste better. He also excelled at growing vegetables and often claimed that his carrots were of such a length, that pit ponies could munch on the ends!

Figure 26: *Gran and Papa, early 1980s*

Gran gained peace and comfort from her spiritualist meetings whether she got a message from 'the other side' or not. Her recollections of these messages never varied in content or consistency. I often heard her say, 'To be a good liar, you must have an excellent memory.' She hated lies with a passion. She truly believed that she had been in touch with her mother and her brother-in-law, Tam Middleton, Auntie Agnes's husband. She also had vivid prophesying dreams. She let me borrow her Doris Stokes books. Doris was a leading psychic and medium at that time; she often appeared on television and on stage. She had the homeliest and kindest of faces. I read all her books, and was moved to tears by some, especially the poetry. I truly wanted to believe what I was reading but couldn't bring myself to say that I truly did believe without question.

One of Gran's dreams that sticks in my mind was one about her dog, Rhona. She had just got in from work and was having forty winks on the sofa when she had a dream about Dad's first Elkhound, Rex mark one (he went on to have Rex mark two and three). Rex was standing with her first Cairn Terrier, also called Rhona (I don't know why, but our family likes to stick with familiar names). In her dream, a Cairn Terrier puppy appeared between the two older dogs. Later that evening she received a call from Miss Murphy, the vet Gran had used in the past. Miss Murphy explained to Gran that she was looking for an owner for a Cairn Terrier puppy which had been destined for America, but the new owners to be decided that she did not have the correct shaped head for showing and breeding purposes and had reneged on the deal. The vet now had a puppy who was looking for a new home. There was no question in Gran's mind that this was the puppy who had come to her in the dream. There was also no question of her not taking the pup. Papa apparently said, 'There will be no more dogs in this house,' but of course his words fell on deaf ears. Papa ultimately loved Rhona just as much as Gran did.

I cannot begin to describe how broken hearted I was when Gran passed away, I had been upset and distressed when my papa had died three years earlier, but this was different. It felt like a part of me had died too, and I couldn't believe I would never see her again. I talked to Gran about every subject under the sun. Nothing was off limits. She had a way of making it seem that everything would be okay. She knew she couldn't solve many of my problems, she also knew that it wasn't her place to do that. She listened and gave sound advice. She was more like a trusted and beloved friend than a grandmother, and I love her with all my heart.

She died in 1991, and it was 2008 before I plucked up the courage to visit a psychic medium.

Figure 27: *My gran with her sisters*

Figure 28: *My great-grandfather, Charles Durnie*

Figure 29: My *Great-Grannie and Granta Heron*

CHAPTER 16

FAMILY TREE

"Why waste your money looking up your family tree? Just go into politics and your opponents will do it for you."

- Mark Twain

I have spent a considerable amount of time researching my family tree. It has been laborious at times, but very rewarding. I now know that I am the twenty-second great-granddaughter of King Robert the Bruce according to one branch of the tree, the twenty-first according to another, but what is a few years between great-grandfathers?

Gran was born Margaret Sawyers-Hogg Durnie, in 1913. She had two brothers, John and David, and three sisters, Caroline 'Carrie', Jemima 'Mima' and Elizabeth 'Bette' who was the youngest. They attended Quarry Brae School in Glasgow when they were children.

During WW2 John and David served in the armed forces. John was in the RAF and reached the rank of Warrant Officer. He became a physiotherapist after the war.

David became the admissions officer for the Victoria Infirmary in Glasgow. He was also an excellent footballer but earned the name 'Dirty Durnie' during his time in Glasgow, Women's factory football teams had become popular, and he coached the McVitie's biscuit factory girls' soccer team.

The Durnie line proved interesting in that my great-grandfather, Charles, was born in Maryland, USA, in 1873. His father had been a partner in a fruit-canning factory, indeed one of the cans with the Durnie name survived until rationing in the Second World War weakened any resolve to keep it. It was opened by my Great Aunt Bette, her son Callum remembers this and by all accounts the fruit was delicious. Why Charles's father sailed from America to Liverpool on the *New England* on the 13th of June 1902 to become a coal miner in Scotland I may never know.

Apparently when the oldest child, Carrie, was informed of the imminent arrival of Aunt Bette, the youngest sibling, she replied, 'To hell with it,' presumably because it would mean more work and less food for her.

Gran and Aunt Bette became domestic servants at the age of fourteen. Gran absolutely hated it but seemed to think that Aunt Bette enjoyed it. That said, Aunt Bette's son Callum remembers his mother covering her occupation on her wedding certificate with a piece of sticky paper.

Gran and her siblings had been taught to dress properly and well. If Gran's employer (at that time in Ardrossan) asked her to go on an errand in her uniform she hated it, not least because the local boys would call out, 'Skivvy!' making her blush with shame and embarrassment.

She adored dancing, but, like most other domestic servants at that time, she was not allowed out at night to attend the local dance halls. However, this did not stop her. She told me, with pride I might add, that she would climb out of her bedroom window and dance the night away, before sneaking very quietly back in through the window which she had left open, to grab a few hours' sleep before the next day's skivvying.

Gran also worked for the Forsythe family in Glasgow. She was employed to cook as well as clean; she was what would have been known as a maid of all work. She remembered being taught how to cook fish properly by the mistress of the house. 'Heat the oil until the smoke turns blue before adding the fish to the pan.'

Possibly, Mrs. Forsythe read that snippet of information in a cookery book. It was common practice for middle-class employers, who found themselves in the financial position to be able to afford domestic staff, to read up about cookery and etiquette and pass it on.

One of the most popular was Isabella Beeton's book of household management, which is still in print today (I have it on my Kindle).

Isabella was only twenty-one years of age when she began her book, which had initially been serialised in her husband's magazine, *The Englishwoman's Domestic Magazine*. Her first contribution appeared in 1859. Eventually, all of the instalments she provided for the magazine were amalgamated into her book which was intended to assist the mistress of the house as well as domestic staff. Isabella is quoted as saying:

"I must frankly own, that if I had known, beforehand, that this book would have cost me the labour which it has, I should never have been courageous enough to commence it. What moved me, in the first instance, to attempt a work like this, was the discomfort and suffering which I had seen brought upon men and women by household mismanagement. I have always thought that there is no more fruitful source of family discontent than a housewife's badly-cooked dinners and untidy ways."

Gran used to say that the only positive thing from being in service was learning correct etiquette for most social occasions which stood her in good stead in the future. I always remember the way she set a table for afternoon tea if visitors were coming, exquisite hand-embroidered table and tea cloths, fine bone china cups and saucers, a cake stand and tea pot. She also used a set of fish knives and forks when they had fish, presumably cooked in blue smoke.

She met my grandfather 'Papa' James Heron when he was a conductor on the buses. He often told the story of seeing my gran walking past his bus, beautifully dressed in her fitted coat, matching hat and gloves. He announced to his driver, 'That is the girl I am going to marry.'

My papa was born in a hamlet in Ayrshire called Moscow, which could cause quite a stir when air travel became popular and he was required to show his passport. The Cold War; a 'geopolitical, ideological and economic struggle between two world superpowers, the USA and the USSR', which had started just after the Second World War in 1947 and lasted until the dissolution of the Soviet Union on the 26th of December 1991, made people more than a tad suspicious of someone born in Moscow.

Gran and Papa married on the 27th of December 1935 in Kilwinning and had three children, Jim (my dad) in 1938, Tom in 1940, and Margaret in 1943.

When war broke out, Papa was refused entry into the armed forces for health reasons; his brothers joined up to fight for their country. John was in the RAF and Tommy was in the army. Billy was in the Chindits, a special force trained in commando methods, who operated behind enemy lines in North Burma in the war against Japan. They were formed and led by Major General Orde Wingate DSO (distinguished service order). For supplies they relied totally on airdrops. Oh, how I wish I had known and asked Uncle Billy about it, but I was too young, and apparently, he never talked about it to anyone. Papa's youngest brother Robert was not old enough to join up.

Papa also had two sisters, Agnes and Margaret, who worked in the nearby ICI munitions factory in Ardeer, near Stevenston in Ayrshire. The factory was protected by barrage balloons during the war. Work involved working with high explosives; the plant produced all of Britain's volatile nitro-glycerine, making it a highly potential target for Nazi bombs. Employees were searched each day to ensure they were not wearing anything made of metal which could cause a spark, and uniforms had ties rather than metal zips or buttons. Dangerous and essential war work indeed.

Figure 30: *Papa on the left with Billy, Tommy and John*

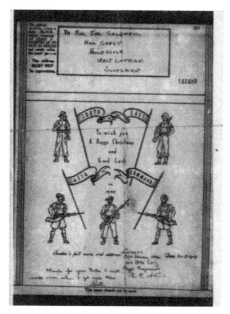

Figure 31: *Postcard sent from Burma by Uncle Billy*

Rationing made life difficult, but, by now, Papa was a long-distance lorry driver and sometimes came home from London with offerings, I think a banana caused quite a stir on one occasion.

One year, Gran had been saving rations for Christmas. She had a sideboard which only locked on one side. She foolishly thought that my dad and Uncle Tom would not figure out how to open the locked side from the unlocked side. On Christmas Day, when she unlocked the sideboard to bring out the half Christmas cake and all the other carefully saved treats, she found that the icing had been picked off the cake. I have already mentioned that Dad was a favourite of his grannie's, being the first grandchild, so Gran was not sure how to react in front of my great-grannie and Grandpa who had been invited for Christmas dinner, until Great-Grannie called out, 'Gie them it,' by way of permission to give them a 'skelp' round the ear.

When Aunt Margaret was born, Gran and Papa were delighted to have a daughter, a little girl who would wear pink and frills, but Auntie M preferred playing with the boys and getting into a mess along with the rest of them so it was not to be. She was also apparently quite outspoken and embarrassed Gran and Papa on several occasions with her honest opinions about some of her aunts and uncles.

Gran always worked, but I mostly remember her at The Craig House. The Craig which is just outside Crosshouse near Laigh Milton Mill, once belonged to the estate of the Mowats of Busbie and later by Captain John Morrice. The original house burned down in 1788 and a new one was built. The Craig was taken over by Strathclyde Regional Council and was used a residential school until 1986. In the early days, it was a boys' school and usually took in underprivileged boys from Glasgow who needed to be looked after, for instance, if a parent was unable to look after them because of ill health or if a parent had been sent to prison. Gran was a seamstress and she mended the boys' clothes, bed linen etc. She tried to explain to me that she mended torn sheets by sewing them 'sides to middle' but I never could get it straight in my head.

I remember going to Christmas parties there and loved looking at the huge house with its spectacular entrance. It was white and had four imposing pillars. They always had a large tree at Christmas, the biggest I had ever seen. We played the usual party games and had sandwiches, sausage rolls and cake. I was incredibly shy though and clung to my gran's coat tails throughout the whole evening, but I did love the whole atmosphere in the big house and loved being in the main part of the house and not just the kitchens and sewing room as was usually the case.

Figure 32: *Craig House when it was a school*

I discovered that my branch of the Heron family tree came to Scotland from Ireland sometime in the early 1800s. They moved to Stoneykirk in Wigtownshire and were primarily farm workers, Byre men, ploughmen and agricultural labourers. This may have coincided with starvation which was prevalent across Europe at the start of the Victorian era. Ireland was dependent on potatoes. They made up approximately 80% of the total Irish diet at that time. Potato blight was the cause of about a third of potato crops being lost in 1845; by 1846 this had risen to three quarters.

W. E. Forster describes whole communities in Ireland *'like walking skeletons, the men stamped with the livid mark of hunger, the children crying in pain, the women in some of the cabins, too weak to stand'*.

Men women and children were found dead or dying in their homes, by the road side and in the workhouses. I find it very painful and heartbreaking to imagine any of my relatives, no matter how distant, suffering like this. My great-grandfather James Heron (Granta as my dad calls him) was born in Scotland, Nethercribben, Holywood in Dumfries in 1882. Granta's father Thomas was born in Wigtownshire in 1861, but Thomas's father, was born in County Down, Ireland, in 1830, so it is more than likely that they moved to Scotland in the hope of finding work and food.

It is one thing to read about these things in history books, quite another thing altogether when you realise your ancestors lived through it, surviving on a diet of potatoes, and then having that one and only source of food taken away. Thankfully, the physical and emotional suffering of being unable to provide food and to watch children starve to death is unimaginable for most of us in the United Kingdom today.

CHAPTER 17

MY UNDERSTANDING OF THE

HERON FAMILY TREE

"If you cannot get rid of the family skeleton, you may as well make it dance."
- George Bernard Shaw

I have spent many long days, weeks and months researching my family tree. The following are two very similar branches that I found. It can get very complicated at times, and often you reach a gut-wrenching dead end after hours and hours of work. That said, I enjoyed it and it became an all-consuming passion. Researching my genealogy is something I have wanted to do since I was eighteen. I was overwhelmed when I found out that I was a descendent of King Robert the Bruce. Although I understand that there may be thousands of people out there who can say the same thing. I read an article in *The Scotsman* recently, written by Alastair Moffat, who said that *'50% of all men who have the surname Stewart or Stuart are the direct descendants of Scotland's long-lasting royal dynasty (who also came to rule over Britain and Ireland).'*

He went on to say, *'Many of these live in Scotland and most do not know that they have royal blood. And it is certain that some men who do not carry the Stewart surname also carry the royal marker, they probably descend from an illegitimate son in an unbroken line.'*

Illegitimate offspring were often unrecognised. They were not seen as a threat because they could not lay claim to the throne. However, many enjoyed a privileged lifestyle, often marrying professional people such as clergymen, others marrying farmers or tradesmen, hence the scattering of the royal genealogy.

It has also been pointed out by Doctor Bruce Durie, that '*Robert I was believed to have had up to a dozen children, several illegitimately*'.

So, statistically, there is a very good chance that my findings are correct. Researching my family tree has led me on a wonderful journey of discovery through Scottish history which I may not have bothered to take otherwise, and for that alone I am grateful.

Dundonald Castle

Dundonald Castle features highly in my family tree. I discovered that several of my ancestors were born and died there.

My brother Alastair lives in Dundonald with his wife Dee and their children Holly and Billy. I am ashamed to admit, that despite living near Dundonald Castle for many years I visited it for the first time last year. The castle offers many activities for locals and visitors alike. Holly and Billy particularly enjoy the Halloween events. Apparently, one year there was a Harry Potter theme complete with games of Quidditch, an owl and ducking for apples, quite a difference from its rich and colourful past.

I read in the Dundonald Castle official souvenir guide book, that there have been three castles on the site where the remains of Dundonald Castle as we know it today stands. Historically, the castles belonged to the High Stewards of Scotland, standing proudly on the conspicuous and ancient hilltop in the village of Dundonald. Unfortunately, there is no existing archaeological evidence of the first timber construction castle, thought to have been built by Walter FitzAlan. Walter who came from Normandy in 1136. By 1160, he was the first High Steward to King David I, and was granted land in Ayrshire as well as other parts of Scotland. The second castle was built between 1240 and 1280 by Alexander Stewart, fourth High Steward of Scotland. Most of the second castle was destroyed during the battles fought for Scottish Independence, between England and

Scotland. Some people believe that Robert the Bruce may have destroyed it to stop it from falling into the hands of the English. One remnant from the second castle is the well, which can be seen as you walk up the (steep) hill towards the castle.

Figure 33: *Jacqueline at Dundonald Castle*

Figure 34: *Dundonald Castle*

The third, three-storey-high castle was built by Robert Stewart, seventh High Steward in 1371, possibly to mark his accession to the throne the same year as Robert the Second of Scotland. Just as a reminder, Robert the Second's grandfather was King Robert the First, 'The Bruce'; his mother was the tragic Marjorie who was thrown from her horse while pregnant with Robert who was born by the first recorded caesarean section in Scottish history. This story affected me so much I feel that I must say a bit more about Marjorie Bruce.

Isabella of Mar died shortly after giving birth to Marjorie in December 1296 at the age of nineteen. Marjorie was the only child of Isabella and King Robert the Bruce; they were apparently very much in love and Robert did not marry again for six years when he took Elizabeth de Burgh to be his wife. There are no records to say who raised Marjorie after her mother died. Her father was passionately fighting to free Scotland from English rule and saw very little of her.

Robert met Elizabeth at the English court and by all accounts she was the daughter of one of Edward I of England's most devoted supporters, Richard the second Earl of Ulster. It has been implied that either Bruce switched loyalties for political gain, or that it was Edward's decision that Bruce should marry the thirteen-year-old Elizabeth in 1302.

On the 27th of March 1306, Robert the Bruce was crowned King of Scotland at Scone, and Marjorie became a Princess of Scotland. Three months later, Bruce was defeated in a battle against Edward I at Methven. Robert sent his wife Marjorie and his two sisters north for safety. The party consisting of Marjorie, her stepmother, two aunts, and Isabella, Countess of Buchan, were escorted by Robert's brother Niall and the Earl of Atholl, was besieged by the English and all of the women were sent to Edward as hostages. Edward then placed Queen Elizabeth de Burgh under house arrest in a manor house in Yorkshire. Marjorie was sent to the Gilbertine convent at Watton. He sent her aunt Christina Bruce to another convent and her aunt Mary Bruce and the Countess of Buchan, who had crowned Robert, were imprisoned in iron and wooden lattice cages exposed to public view, Mary at Roxburgh Castle, and the Countess at Berwick Castle where she was treated like an animal on view to all and sundry. Edward kept her there for nearly four years until he relented in 1310 and sent her to the House of the Carmelite nuns at Berwick. The Earl of Atholl was hanged and his head was displayed on London Bridge. Niall was hung, drawn and quartered.

Marjorie endured solitary confinement for four years which was the lesser of two evils. A cage had been built for her at the Tower of London, but Edward decided against it and sent her to the convent instead.

In 1314, King Robert the Bruce defeated Edward at the battle of Bannockburn. He took many hostages and exchanged the most important prisoners for the release of his family. Marjorie was betrothed to Walter Stewart, sixth Lord High Stewart as a reward for his commendable conduct during the battle. They were married in 1315.

In March 1316, a heavily pregnant Marjorie went riding. Her horse was startled and threw her to the ground causing a dislocation of her neck. She went into premature labour and her son Robert, who became Robert II, King of Scots, was born by caesarean section in Paisley Abbey. Marjorie died a few hours later, though in reality, I suspect much sooner than that. Just like her mother before her, she was nineteen years old. She was buried at Paisley Abbey. Marjorie's descendants include the House of Stuart and all their successors on the throne of Scotland, England and the United Kingdom. Truth is indeed stranger than fiction. What a tragic life poor Marjorie had.

Meanwhile, back at the castle! The ruins of the barmkin wall (courtyard wall) are clear to see as you approach the tower of the castle. The barmkin, or courtyard, would have housed the bakehouse, brewhouses, stables, smithy and suchlike. When the King was in residence this would have been a bustling hive of activity. The ground floor at that time was comprised of cellars, traditionally used for storage of foodstuff, grain, bread and dairy produce plus wine and fuel.

When you walk into the castle, you can see the impressive high stone vaulted hall ceiling. The first floor housed the Laigh Hall, or lower hall, which was an impressive reception room, reached now by what was once the servants' staircase. There was a minstrel's gallery and today you can still see a latrine closet which would have been used by the musicians. The King would have sat on a raised platform with favoured guests on either side of him. The King would have had the only proper chair, everyone else would have made do with wooden stools or benches. The castle also had two prisons, a pit prison used for prisoners of low status, and another used for prisoners awaiting trial by the King in the Laigh Hall.

The Great Hall was designed to indicate the high-ranking status of the King, and impress visitors to the castle. Ribs and arches of the barrel-vaulted ceiling can be clearly seen today, as can the outline of the original fireplace. The Great Hall would have been used for high-status banquets and meetings.

Little evidence of the upper floor and roof has survived.

Robert had a large family. He established them as powerful noblemen and women either by their own right or by marriage. Robert passed the responsibility of his kingdom to his sons from about the age of fifty-five. He died at Dundonald in 1390 aged about seventy-four and was one of the longest-lived Scottish monarchs.

As Robert's sons and daughters were becoming established elsewhere, the castle occupants moved to nearby Auchens House/Castle about 1630. Auchens was an impressive mansion set near Dundonald woods, which, incidentally, have the most extensive areas of elm dominated woodland in Ayrshire, as well as ash, oak and sycamore.

The Auchens estate was originally owned by the Wallaces of Dundonald. Colonel James Wallace, who was the last of the Wallaces to live there, passed the estate to his relative Sir William Cochrane in 1640. The Colonel died in exile in 1678 following the Battle of Rullion Green in the Pentland Hills where he had led a group of Covenanters, rebel soldiers, against the Scottish Royal Army led by Sir Thomas (Tam) Dalyell of the Binns, 1st Baronet. He was also known as "Bluidy Tam".

Lady Susanna Montgomery, Countess of Eglinton, who was born in Culzean Castle in 1690, died in Auchens on the 18th of March 1790, age ninety.

The building was used as a German prisoner of war camp during the First World War.

As I say, I feel very ashamed that all this rich history had been right there on my doorstep for many years without me knowing about it. I am so grateful that researching my family tree has enlightened me about my local Scottish history and heritage.

CHAPTER 18

IMAGINING A DAY IN THE LIFE OF GREAT-GRANTA AND GRANNY HERON

"Call it a clan, call it a network, call it a tribe, call it a family: Whatever you call it, whoever you are, you need one."

- Jane Howard

No matter what day of the week, hail, rain or shine, if I need to wash some clothes, it is a simple matter of going to the laundry basket, putting the clothes in the washing machine, taking them out when the cycle is finished and either hanging them out to dry or tumble drying them. End of story!

For my great-granny, wash day started on a Monday and went on until about Thursday!

Sometimes heavily soiled clothes would be soaked on a Saturday in preparation for the beginning of the working week.

She had to get out of bed a few of hours earlier than usual to light the fire to boil kettles and pans of water; her usual day would have started at dawn!

She would probably have collected water either from a stream or a well. Although some well to do town houses in Edwardian times had running water, water closets, and even electricity, it would be some time before such luxuries would reach country folk.

The only items to help her would have been a "dolly" which was a wooden handle with what looked like a child's stool attached, a wringer if she was lucky and some washing soda which was very harsh and irritated the skin, making hands red and sore.

I suspect she would have placed larger items like sheets over hedges and bushes if the outdoor line was full. In the winter and on wet days she would most likely have had a "pulley" which was usually four lengths of wood attached to each other by a bracket at the ends which could be hoisted up to the ceiling of the kitchen using a rope. In fact, I used a pulley in our house in North Berwick. When the kitchen window was open, and the wind blew inside, nappies and clothes dried very quickly!

Once the clothes were dry there was starching and ironing, using a very heavy, flat iron warmed on the kitchen range.

Cooking and even heating water was a major chore. It would have been done on the range which needed to be kept stocked with fuel, black leaded and cleaned. Probably the first thing Granny did after rising at dawn (which in winter would have been freezing cold) and dressing in the many required Edwardian layers of clothing, was to venture into the kitchen and light the fire in the range. Without the fire, there would be no hot water and no hot food.

Baking could not be done until the afternoon when the oven was warm enough, and in fact there may even still have been a communal oven in the village where women could take pies and bread to be baked marked with their initials, hence the nursery rhyme: 'Pat a cake pat a cake baker's man, bake me a cake as fast as you can, pat it and prick it and mark it with B and put it in the oven for baby and me.'

I know she was good at baking, I can remember her delicious shortbread and buttermilk scones, and her wonderful almost black, glossy bramble jelly.

There would have been an outside privy, basically a hole in the ground, with a wooden seat above it and a shed-like building surrounding it. The door would have had a gap top and bottom to allow fresh air to circulate. A chamber pot would have been used by the family at night to prevent a cold, dark trip out to the back yard.

Human waste was mixed with animal dung and straw to help it

break down into manure.

The walls were usually whitewashed which as well as brightening up the privy also helped to kill germs. Whitewash was made from a solution of limestone, and the wooden seat was most likely sterilised with caustic soda. There was no toilet paper; squares of newspaper were cut into squares and strung together at one corner to be hung on a nail or hook. A common saying at the time was that the cheap magazines around at the time were nothing but "bum fodder".

I expect Granny and Granta brushed their teeth using a bone brush with badger bristle and soot!

Soot acted as an abrasive paste when mixed with water and apparently made a very good job of keeping teeth clean, obviously minus the minty taste!

Cleaning the cottage would have been an unforgiving and heavy task for Granny; mud plus animal dung would inevitably be trailed over her floor on heavy 'tackety' work boots.

I am certain Granny would have washed using a bowl and cloth; baths tended to be for children and men and involved collecting and boiling copious amounts of water. There was also the matter of a lack of privacy in a small farm worker's cottage.

After the dirty jobs, Granny would have made breakfast for Granta coming in from his first jobs of the day, probably about eight a.m. It was common at that time to have porridge, potato, small amounts of bacon, onion and bread. Everyone had labour-intensive jobs and they needed to fill up for energy.

Granny would have spent a long time just fetching water throughout the day, perhaps collecting dry kindling for the fire, cleaning, cooking and looking after chickens and poultry if they kept any. It was also common to keep maybe one pig which again would have been up to Granny to look after.

By Edwardian times shops had quite a selection of branded foods thanks to the railways, some of which we which we still use today – Coleman's mustard, Typhoo tea, Tate and Lyle golden syrup and treacle, Brasso and Sunlight soap to name but a few! Granny would go to the local village shop when she needed any provisions, although I am not certain how far this would have been for her or how often she would have gone, but with no fridge or freezer I suspect it was quite often. I am sure Granny would have been adept at salting, smoking and pickling food to preserve it.

Sheep's head stew was a common, filling and nutritious dish at the time. When an animal was killed for food, nothing was left to waste; every bit of it was used, including the fat to make tallow candles, and of course the hide to make leather in the local tannery not to mention wool.

Blacksmiths, candle makers and shoe makers were commonplace although by Edwardian times mass produced shoes and boots were available and many shoe makers had become cobblers. Probably the most mass-produced footwear at that time were the boots made for soldiers fighting in the Great War of 1914-1918.

Basically, eating food in season was the order of the day (which thankfully has come back into fashion). Being on a farm I am sure there would have been no shortage of milk, and therefore butter and cheese although Granny probably had to make the latter two.

It is almost certain that Granny and Granta would have had a vegetable plot, growing root vegetables such as carrots, turnip, beetroot and parsnips. I suspect that potatoes and oats would have been grown on the farm land, cheap imports of wheat meant that it was no longer a viable crop to grow.

Oats could also be used to feed livestock without which, most farm work would have been impossible at that time, although some automation was being introduced it was expensive, noisy and sometimes unreliable.

Making hay while the sun shines was no joke. If the hay got damp and wasted there was no way to feed cattle and sheep in the winter months.

Horses needed to be seen by a farrier about every six weeks to ensure they were healthy and not in danger of becoming lame.

Great-Granta's first job of the day was most likely to feed the animals. Meat and dairy farming were most profitable in the 1900s.

Like Granny, he would have brushed his teeth with a bone and badger brush and soot; his razor would have been the open, cut-throat type!

Working with unguarded agricultural machinery available to him at the time was not for the faint hearted. There was no such thing as Health and Safety as we know it today!

Granta's working day would have begun at dawn, probably returning later in the morning, say eight a.m., for some breakfast once the range was warm enough!

The attitude with agricultural workers, as with any other manual workers at that time, was "accidents happen". Compensation would not have been comprehended.

You had to work to eat, work came with risks, the risks had to be lived with and accepted. Failure to provide for your family could end in the workhouse with husbands, wives and children being separated living a life of misery and drudgery.

Many agricultural workers suffered from pneumonia, bronchitis, arthritis and chilblains of the hands and feet.

In Great-Granta's case, he lost an arm!

He would have spent many hours ploughing fields and planting crops, using a horse-drawn plough. I can almost hear him call out, 'Come by,' (turn left) and, 'Come around,' (turn right). To the shire horses.

In 1903, the first tractor was introduced the Ivel agricultural engine, but as previously mentioned it was expensive and very noisy. Only 500 were sold worldwide at a cost of £300 each which was about the equivalent of six years' wages.

Granta would also need to use a kibbler to grind down cereal to feed livestock.

Not only would he have made hay, but he would have had to provide a dry store to keep it safe throughout the winter. Hay lofts were most common, but the roof would have required maintenance.

In the absence of a chimney sweep, he may have cut down a bush, such as holly to pull through the chimney to loosen the soot.

He would have returned home at around one o'clock for dinner and a catch up of the day so far.

In the evenings after tea, Granta would probably have enjoyed a pint of beer or ale, often this was someone's front room if there was no actual public house in the village.

Great-Granny and Granta had seven children – my papa, James born on the first of May 1913, Tommy, Agnes, John, William, Margaret and Robert.

What it was like for them to feed and clothe seven children when life was so hard I can only begin to imagine.

My life seems to be somewhat self-indulgent and wasteful by comparison.

Dad remembers that Granta could tie his neck tie and shoelaces as well as any able-bodied man and could out dig anyone in the garden.

Great-Granta died in Kilmarnock Infirmary in 1964 age eighty-two years. I was four years old.

CHAPTER 19

COUSIN CALLUM, MOSCOW TALES

"The strongest of all warriors are these two — Time and Patience."
- Leo Tolstoy, *War and Peace*

I have contacted many members of my family to find out more about relatives within living memory. Stories, anecdotes, photographs and documentation, I had not seen or heard before were forthcoming, it was remarkable and heartwarming.

My dad's cousin Callum was particularly helpful; he offered an amazing insight to his noteworthy past. Known as Callum to the Heron family, James McCallum Manderson to everyone else, has many colourful tales to tell.

When I was growing up I heard it mentioned that Callum had spent some time in Russia, but that was as far as it went. I had always yearned to find out more. When I started to research my family tree I contacted Callum and asked him about his memories. They were much more fascinating than I could have imagined.

Callum was in the Scots Guards. He was stationed in Hampshire and London after returning from Libya in May 1960. While he was in the battalion headquarters, a teleprint came through from the Foreign Office which mentioned a proposed appointment for two military men as personal attendants to the ambassador at the British embassy in Moscow. This was at the height of the Cold War, and Callum was unable to resist the challenge.

He made an application and consequently was interviewed in Carlton House Terrace, just off The Mall in Westminster, by the Ambassador Designate Sir Frank Roberts, and was duly appointed. Sir Frank was keen to have a military presence at the embassy when he was in residence. Because of Russian rules, all the household staff was Russian; this meant that Sir Frank and his wife were virtually left alone in the large stately home opposite the Kremlin outside working hours with just one British security officer in the main hall.

Callum met his colleague-to-be, Irish Guards NCO Jim Moriarty at that interview (they are still in touch). Both men were accepted and began to prepare for the posting. Callum remembers them being kitted out with arctic clothing, tropical military clothing and two civilian suits, and within a week, he and Jim were on a three-hour, British European Airways comet flight, from Heathrow to Moscow.

On arrival at Sheremetyevo Airport in Moscow, passengers were asked to remain in their seats because a Russian frontier officer was coming on board the aircraft to examine passports. They were informed that any who did not satisfy him would remain on board and return to the UK.

The officer looked superbly smart in a powder blue, beautifully tailored greatcoat which sported red and gold epaulettes, and according to Callum the officer began to theatrically examine the passports by looking at each one and then tossing it over his shoulder to be caught by one of his two assistants. He then turned around and smilingly said, 'Welcome to Russia.'

At the arrivals lounge Callum and Jim were met by the ambassador's personal assistant and they were taken to the embassy in the ambassadorial Rolls-Royce.

Callum was briefed about the dos and don'ts shortly after arrival, one example being no serious fraternising with the Russian people, male or female, as doing so could result in arrest and imprisonment in Russia or deportation and possible court martial. Afterwards on the table of his room, he found a brown envelope with his name and regimental number on it. Inside was an invitation to a military reception at the Kremlin. He was unable to attend.

I will let Callum continue with his story in his own words:

Sometime into my service a new military attaché (our official boss) took up his post viz Brigadier Lee Maxwell.

An absolutely great chap, who dispensed with rank by addressing us by our first names.

Since I was James, Lee Maxwell always called me 'Jimmy'. Imagine a private soldier being addressed as Jimmy by a Brigadier!

Sir Frank and Lady Roberts would not be coming to the embassy for another two weeks or so, therefore it was up to us to familiarise ourselves with the surroundings, and we were free to go out and visit the city but only during daylight hours at this stage.

It seemed obvious that there would need to be some 'housework' required since the official reception room, known as the white room, was covered in dust. Most of the Russian household staff was on leave until Sir Frank's arrival, so it did look as if we had been landed with a couple of chores to say the least. However, being guardsmen, we knew well the old adage, *"Join the army and see the world... Join the guards and clean it!"*

Figure 35: *British Embassy, Moscow*

During this period, I went out a few times during the day and was told by the main hall security guards that it was very pleasurable to go and eat out in any of the splendid hotels where you could get caviar on toast, borscht soup, genuine chicken Kiev, and the best ice cream in the world and all for around £1!! I did this several times needless to say.

As the days went by it came home to me that Muscovites could dine in this grand manner in hotels and restaurants, and yet the same people had to queue daily in the shops for bread, meat and indeed every other item of food. It brought back post-war memories at home in Glasgow during the late 1940s when similar queues could be seen outside every food shop. The difference being in Russia there was no rationing! To add to the hardship Russian champagne was the equivalent of 25 pence a bottle.

And yet meat was seldom seen in the shops and the arrival of cheese and butter was quite a special event for the queues. Altogether very sad for the 1960s.

In going around Moscow and eating out, I soon began to pick up the rudiments of the language which came in very handy in dealing with the Russian household staff.

Sir Frank and Lady Roberts arrived just about a couple of weeks after we did as I recall.

He was fifty-three years old. I don't know how old Her Ladyship was at that time but possibly not all that far behind him in years. She was Arab; her godfather was old King Feisal of Iraq (Lawrence of Arabia's old ally). They met in Cairo when he was there in the 1930s. Before coming to Moscow, Sir Frank had been the British representative in NATO.

Sir Frank had served at the embassy in Moscow during World War Two and had established good relations with the Russians during that time.

Soon after the arrival of Sir Frank and Lady Roberts we were called to their apartment. This was of course after Sir Frank had seen and met all his senior embassy staff.

As mentioned earlier, the living, social and guest rooms were on the floors above the embassy offices.

Sir Frank smilingly welcomed us and explained that the main reason for our being there was that he had lived and worked at the embassy during the war (it being in effect a stately home directly opposite the Kremlin) and he had realised that when the staff vacated after work it would be completely empty.

The rooms were huge, ballroom size and superbly furnished with genuine antiques. The house had originally belonged to a sugar tycoon in the early 1800s.

He said that there were no particular jobs dreamed up for us at this time, but these duties would soon materialise when the Russian household staff arrived at the end of the week.

He explained that a lot of 'discreet overseeing' would have to be done since although a Russian person might be engaged for domestic duty, who was to know that that was the true reason for their presence?

Sir Frank then added that he was going to the Kremlin in the morning to present his credentials to Mr. Khrushchev. Dan, my colleague, asked him what he would be wearing to the Kremlin and Sir Frank said that he would just be wearing the suit he now had on since there was no time to unpack as he had papers and documents to read through.

Dan and I looked at one another and said, 'Sir, as Guards it will be our duty to ensure that you are turned out impeccably at all times.'

After he stopped chuckling, Sir Frank said, 'Are you sure, chaps?'

So, it goes without saying that thereafter the British ambassador turned heads with the excellence of his immaculate turnout.

As time passed, we were often called upon to assist at our embassy's receptions, for example when some head of state would be arriving with a large retinue or indeed during festivals; for example, Moscow hosted the International Film Festival in 1961, also cultural occasions when there would be a couple of hundred guests at least. Dan and I, again always in uniform with which we were always comfortable, would circulate the guests topping up their champagne glasses for example. So, Dan and I had the 'dreadful drudgery' of pouring champagne and going around enjoying occasional chat, although strictly speaking conversing was not encouraged.

Prior to a function of that type, on the day and about thirty minutes before the first guests were due to arrive, either Dan or I would be stationed at the entrance to the embassy's main hall where we would either inspect invitations or take the cloaks or coats from the guests and hanging them in a recess. (The coats, not the guests!)

One day there was a reception at our embassy during the 1961 Moscow Film Festival and various international stars were due. It was my turn to do the invitation inspections. Various Russian, international and Hollywood stars arrived, which in itself was a most enjoyable period. Just as I was about to go upstairs, since I thought that I had exhausted the guest list, I saw a scruffy figure appear at the door. It was man wearing a crumpled suit that looked slept in, and it appeared as if he had not shaved for a week at least.

I stood in front of him and said, 'May I see your invitation please?' No way was I expecting one. There was always a gate crasher or two at such receptions.

He looked at me and mumbled that he might just have remembered to bring it. At long last he pulled out the badly crumpled invitation card and I read the name.

'Her Majesty's Ambassador requests the pleasure of the company of Mr. Peter Finch'. Enough said. Unkempt, shabbily dressed, and yet the female guests were still enchanted with his charming presence. Indeed, a true star. Whist I was assisting Peter upstairs to the guest-filled White Room, one of one of the loveliest stars of her day or indeed any other time, Gina Lollobrigida, appeared the door dressed in the most fantastic gown which really made her look like a goddess. Please remember I was only a twenty-three-year-old star-struck lad. But even today I still worship her. A star-struck eighty-one-year-old!

I saw that there was now only one invitee outstanding. Elizabeth Taylor.

Just then the Brigadier appeared asking me to hurry up and get involved with the drinks, adding that Ms. Taylor was noted for late arrival in order to create her usual star entrances.

Just as he said that, in came the great Liz herself followed by a rather commonplace fellow clutching her handbag. He looked familiar, and then hearing his voice I realised it was the great Eddie

Fisher, her husband.

As Ms. Taylor approached, apart from her striking beauty, I was struck by her sparkling eyes which were virtually hypnotic. I then flunked my duty; I did not ask for their invitations. Who would? Then, what hit me was that Liz was wearing a model gown uncannily similar to the dress that Gina had arrived in.

I proceeded to circulate the party refilling glasses. After about ten minutes one of the Russian staff members came up to me pointing downwards to the carpet whispering hoarsely, 'Downstairs, downstairs.'

I immediately thought there must be an incident in the entrance hall. I left the White Room and ran down the stairs three at a time. There was Liz Taylor demanding her wrap which I managed to place on her before she stormed out through the front door, with Eddie close behind her, to her chauffeured car and away. Liz Taylor was renowned for her barrack room language; she certainly made me blush that day!

Next day I was on duty and Lady Roberts was hosting at the embassy the showing of the British entry to the film festival – 'A Taste of Honey' starring the great Dora Bryan and the excellent Rita Tushingham. I was in the room merely to provide the customary aperitifs to the guests should they so wish.

The movie in my opinion showed the average Brit to be some sort of lowlife and I felt as if it was really the dreariest film I had ever seen. This was probably due to the fact that the room being used as a cinema was quite small and so therefore, I had to sit through it three times!

Figure 36: *Callum outside the Embassy, opposite The Kremlin*

Last Months at the Embassy

In mid-1962 I had struck up acquaintance with an American chap whom I knew as Carl.

It was obvious that he was of security orientation, as it were, stationed of course at the US embassy, but on a temporary basis it would seem.

We got on well and curiously, every so often, he would appear to go off somewhere else for several days. Curiosity getting the better of me, I asked if he could tell me where he went.

He smiled and said that he was 'doing a round' of concentration camps in Eastern Europe where it seemed he was taking notes and where possible, photos.

I then assumed he was writing a book. I mentioned this to him, and he smiled and made no comment other than that he felt there was a family need.

I said no more for I felt that it was a touchy subject for him. I casually asked him to spell his surname. Again, he smiled and said it was Schindler.

At that time, of course it meant nothing to me.

Carl asked if I would be free to be with him next day. 'Who do I have to do?' I said!

'Pour a few drinks for Benny Goodman and his band,' Carl replied. I attended Benny Goodman's two Moscow concerts, to packed houses, I might add. Carl departed along with the band who were continuing their tour of the USSR.

Carl and I continued to keep in touch for a couple of years after that, and then one day he wrote from Virginia and said that he was off on a job, but would he get back to me after three months. I never heard from him again.

In September 1961 I had an offer from a visitor from London who had been enquiring through appropriate channels about visiting the scene of the charge of the light brigade at Balaclava. He felt that being military I might like to join him.

We flew to Kiev (£8 return), Prior arrangements had been made to provide transport for our journey to the Crimea. Unfortunately, at that time we could not take photographs. However, the frontier guards at the site were very friendly, and in company of two of them, we walked the length of the Valley of Death, just over a mile.

Naturally, but perhaps naively, I was looking for old cannon balls and bones etc., but there was no sign of anything like that, and then, walking down the central area I did see the odd horseshoe lying here and there and I thought, *Perhaps?* I asked one of the frontier chaps if I could have one. He looked at me, put his finger to his lips to say, 'Hush,' but smiled and nodded his head. When we left for our flight back, I was handed a little paper-wrapped parcel.

I still have that horseshoe hanging over our back door at home.

I am of course very well aware that it might have been from a local agricultural horse, however I chose to feel that it might still be from a soldier in the UK whose horse went down with him on that day.

Forgive the sentimentality but that's how we old soldiers get.

*

I cannot tell you how much I enjoyed interviewing Callum and hearing about his time in Moscow. He has a certain way of telling a tale which is why chose to use his own words, mine would not do them justice.

I must add that the Moscow Embassy is where Callum met the love of his life, Christine, who was working there with the foreign office. They have been married for fifty-five years and counting!

Callum also told me about his work in London.

In 1963, upon his return to the UK, Callum went directly from the embassy to the war office in London. In 1971, having moved to local government two or three years earlier, he became the town clerk of St Ives Borough Council in Cambridgeshire.

In 1984 he applied for the post of Chief Administration Officer with the City of London Police.

The post was available because of a move by the Home Office to civilianise senior officer posts to facilitate these officers to return to police duties. He commenced duty at Old Jewry, the city police headquarters in April 1984.

The City force is of course one of the two London forces, the other being the much larger Metropolitan Police. The City of London Police covered the historic square mile of the City of London with a very versatile and internationally renowned fraud squad. Staff for which Callum was responsible numbered just under 500, and not only included administrative people but also catering, housing, domestic, traffic wardens etc., and of course staff at Old Bailey.

Amusingly, Callum told me that at one time during his work there, the Commissioner, Owen Kelly, Assistant Commissioner Bill Taylor and Chief Superintendent Bob Fowlie and Callum as deputy to Bob, were all Scots. Accordingly, they were apparently sometimes referred to by chaps in the Met as 'The City of London Scottish'.

Callum explained that the work was varied, extremely so, sometimes very tense, sometimes very worrying, but after work, the off-duty times were more than enjoyable.

Although he worked exclusively for the police, he was in fact an officer of the Corporation of London, and sometimes the Corporation would require senior corporation staff to officiate as ushers during royal occasions, banquets, etc.

He told me that he had had the pleasure of escorting such personalities as Ted Heath, Jim Callaghan, and Harold Wilson to their appointed places before their being presented to foreign potentates.

He also had the privilege of dining in Guildhall when banquets were arranged. He laughingly said that although he could be at the service end, he always had the pleasure of mixing, albeit remotely, with the likes of likes of Ronald Reagan, Mr. Gorbachev and the King of Morocco as well as being close up at times to Her Majesty the Queen and the Duke of Edinburgh. Oh, and apparently, the food was very good too!

In November 1984 after seven months in the post Callum was granted the Freedom of the City of London.

He was also presented to Princess Anne. She was guest of honour and speaker at one of his Officers' Mess Lunches in the 1980s. She is allegedly rather good at telling jokes!

Callum and his wife Christine also had the honour of attending one of the royal garden parties at Buckingham Palace in the summer of 1989, and were presented to HRH, Princess Diana, 'a lovely lady', at Guildhall.

And to think that I would not have known about any of this had I not decided to research my family tree.

Figure 37: *Callum with his wife Christine and Princess Diana*

Figure 38: *Callum in the Czar's garden*

CHAPTER 20

GOING TO AMERICA

"Everyone must have a shot at the American Dream."
- Howard Schultz

"It was the best of times, it was the worst of times."
- Charles Dickens, *A Tale of Two Cities*

In 1999, an opportunity arose for us to move to America for a couple of years. The timing wasn't great; Jemma was in fifth year at high school and had important exams coming up. Both girls were in the school orchestra and were heavily involved with the school's drama group. The house was always full of activity and chatter as friends came and went, rehearsing for this and that, but I was certain that it would be much better to look back saying that we gave it a go rather than, 'I wonder what it would have been like.' After numerous discussions, we decided that we would take the bull firmly by the horns and go. There was a lot to do; we needed to rent out our house for a start and get Bracken up to speed with his rabies immunisations. We decided it would be better if OH went ahead in September and that I would stay behind with the kids until the following spring allowing Jemma to sit her exams. Unknown to us at the time, that decision was the beginning of the end of our marriage.

We found ourselves living what was known as Bloomington-Normal, in McLean County Illinois. Bloomington and Normal are two cities adjacent to each other and are sometimes called The Twin Cities. We were fortunate to move to a house in Ironwood Country Club Drive which was in the Normal Community West High School catchment area. I had heard that they had an excellent music department and had hoped that the girls could go there. It was an excellent school, and a pleasant area to live, but the time apart had changed OH and me irrevocably and it was not the happy exciting experience I had envisaged. We became different people, and we wanted different things. I felt like I was living with a stranger and I think he felt the same.

My biggest priority, and challenge, was making sure the girls were happy and settling into their new school and new lifestyle. It wasn't easy, for any of us. I became deeply unhappy and very lonely. I had come from a town where I practically knew everyone, had a wide circle of friends and colleagues, to being almost invisible and superfluous to requirements, even at home. I was so thankful that Bracken was with us. He would allow me to bury my head in his soft black fur and sob until I could sob no more.

I was determined to make the best of our great American adventure. The house was great. The estate had been built around a golf course, so it was a bit like home from home in that I could see golfers and golf carts from the windows. We had four bedrooms, three of which had walk-in closets, bliss. OH, and I had an en-suite with a large jacuzzi bath and a walk-in closet so big, that it could have been used as a fifth bedroom, it was amazing. The house also had a triple garage and a huge basement. I had never had so much storage space. We rarely used the front door, but when we did, we entered a tiled hall which had a large coat closet. The dining room was immediately on the left which in turn opened into a small sitting room. The sitting room, which became known as 'Mum's reading room' and was furnished with warm yellow chairs, led directly into the kitchen. The kitchen opened into a large dining area. There was a step down into a generous family room which had a large stone fireplace complete with log fire. Off the small dining area was a door which led to the utility room and garage. The utility room had a large top-loading washing machine with matching tumble drier. It also had a fold-down ironing board. I would often hang out my washing much to the amusement and maybe annoyance of my neighbours. I could only hang out washing in early spring and autumn; any other time of the year was either way too hot and humid, or freezing. Another door led to the huge, finished basement. I was to spend quite a bit of time in the basement because the computer was in there, and also it was our shelter when the tornado sirens went off, which could be frequent at certain times of the year. Next to the utility room was a toilet. There were also sliding patio doors which led out to a deck, a patio and a large garden, part of which was fenced off which was unusual for the area which was open plan. There was a small creek at the bottom of the garden, with the golf course adjacent.

Thankfully, the girls got settled into a routine and met some good friends. I would often drive them to school to avoid the embarrassment of the yellow school bus. Typically, older students drove to school. I began to get involved with school activities. Again, both girls were in the school orchestra and choir, and they joined the drama group. Parents were encouraged to help with costumes, scenery, and fundraising; it was a great way to meet other parents and make some friends of my own. One fundraising venture required me to call a list of parents at home. This turned out to be problematic in that either the person I called loved my accent and kept me talking on the phone for ages, or they couldn't understand what I was saying and would hang up thinking it was some sort of hoax call. After that unusual experience, I made a point of saying that I was happy to do anything to help, but not if it involved making phone calls. My Scottish accent seemed to cause quite a stir wherever I went. Normal was not a tourist attraction, so as a family we were quite a novelty. I remember being in Wal-Mart and the girl on the checkout asked about my 'amazing accent'. I explained that I was from Scotland and had been in the States for about six months. She looked at me open mouthed and said, 'Wow, you are doing great, I can understand everything you are saying.' Another shop assistant in a beautiful shop called Von Maur, asked me if I had been able to speak English before I had come to America. It was the Scottish bit they seemed to struggle with. If anyone asked if I was British, I would say yes straight away, but if they asked if I was English, I felt duty bound to explain that I was from Scotland, not England, but that it was all part of the United Kingdom. This was usually where the trouble started. Nonetheless, they seemed to love the accent and would often ask me just to talk which was a little disconcerting at times.

I loved driving in America; it just seemed to come naturally to me to drive on the other side of the road. Notice I say 'other' and not 'wrong'. My American son-in law might object to the word 'wrong' and rightly so.

I was reading the local paper, *The Pantagraph* (yup, those local papers again) and noticed that there was going to be a refresher course for senior citizens who were re-sitting their driving test. I was allowed to drive using my UK licence for six months but knew I would need to sit the Department of Motor Vehicles test eventually. In Illinois, between the ages of twenty-one and eighty, you renew your driving licence every four years using the Safe Driver Renewal scheme which involves taking a sight test and paying a renewal fee. Over the age of seventy-five you must also take another driving test. This is reduced to two years from the ages of eighty-one and eighty-six, and annually after the age of eighty-seven. The written test consists of thirty-five questions. You are required to answer at least twenty-eight correctly to pass. The questions are a mixture of identifying traffic signs and signals, understanding traffic laws and driving safety rules, vehicle equipment and crash prevention. The refresher course did exactly what it said on the tin and was perfect for me. I caused quite a stir when I entered the room being the only person under the age of seventy-five, but it was the best thing I could have done. We were talked through the requirements and given examples of test papers. I left the class and drove straight to the test centre, had my vision test, sat the written paper, went for a short drive with an examiner and duly passed. I got thirty-five out of thirty-five thanks to my class!

It came as a bit of a shock when I realised that teenagers could be issued with an instruction permit between the ages of fifteen and seventeen so long as they were enrolled in a State-approved driver's education course. Normal Community West High School offered Driver's Ed as part of the curriculum, so Jemma was eligible. Lisa wasn't fifteen yet, thank goodness. I must say I was impressed with the system. Teen drivers under the age of eighteen had to provide written verification that they had undertaken at least fifty hours of driving instruction, ten of which had to have been at night. There were also under-eighteen driving restrictions in that anyone under the age of eighteen could not drive alone between the hours of ten p.m. and six a.m. Sunday to Thursday, eleven p.m. and six a.m. Fridays and Saturdays. Also, people who had been injured in a car accident, sometimes very badly injured, were invited to speak to the students during their driver's education classes. I still felt my heart thumping in my chest the first time I watched Jemma and Lisa drive off in the car together.

Figure 39: *Winter in Ironwood*

CHAPTER 21

TWO NATIONS DIVIDED BY

A COMMON LANGUAGE

'If you can't say something nice, don't say nothin' at all.'
- Thumper, Walt Disney's *Bambi*

I decided to volunteer at the Community Health Care Clinic which was situated on Franklin Avenue in Normal. There had been an advert in *The Pantagraph* asking for help, so I decided to offer my services. I had previously volunteered to teach English to foreign students, mainly Hispanic people, but found myself wholeheartedly agreeing with the person who once said that Britain and America were *'two nations divided by a common language'* (it was either Oscar Wilde, George Bernard Shaw or Sir Winston Churchill depending on which version you read). I explained the difference between two pictures of a pencil to a student. I told him one was sharp, and one was blunt. I was corrected by my supervisor and told that it was not blunt, it was dull. It became a bit of a minefield and I found that I was being taught just as much as the students.

The free medical clinic offered a valuable service for under or uninsured people in Bloomington-Normal. When I worked there, there was one full-time paid nurse, everyone else was a volunteer. A rota of doctors provided evening clinics three times a week. There was a pharmacy and the drugs were provided by pharmaceutical companies free of charge, likewise, local pharmacies like Walgreens and Wal-Mart provided over the counter drugs, often nearing their expiration dates.

I was covered to work there by The Good Samaritan Law which provides basic legal protection for individuals who aid people who are injured or in danger. Each US State has its own version, but the Illinois statute says:

Any licensed medical professional, who in good faith, provides emergency care without fee to a person, shall not, as a result of his or her acts or omissions, except wilful or wanton misconduct on the part of the person, in providing the care, be liable for civil damages.

New patients were asked to read and sign the decree. They were also required to provide evidence of their insurance or rather lack of it. Many people were working, but could not afford to buy adequate health insurance, some were between insurances. I vividly remember one woman who was in floods of tears. She told me that she had always worked and bought insurance, but her husband had cancer which required expensive treatment leaving nothing in the insurance pot for her treatment. Very sad. It made me very proud of and thankful for our own National Health Service which can be much maligned and taken for granted by some people.

McClean County Medical Society, local businesses and religious organisations acknowledged the growing requirement for medical care for some people who were 'slipping through the cracks' and together they founded the Community Health Clinic in 1993. It was and still is a pleasant building to work in and is run by a dedicated team of men and women who want to give something to the community. Once a month the volunteers would bring an assortment of homemade food and treats to share while we mingled and got to know each other. I took coronation chicken one time which I had made from scratch for the first and last time ever. It took me ages but went down a storm.

One matter needed to be addressed by me. Writing the date. I had caused some confusion by writing 04/05/01 and not 05/04/01 (or was it the other way around?). Either way, I had to get used to writing the date by putting the month first and then the day to avoid unnecessary confusion in patient notes.

I found myself on the receiving end of health care when I fell and smashed my wrist into five pieces one morning while I was out walking Bracken. It happened after a long spell of a particularly nasty episode of back pain, involving a herniated disc and annular tears. We were very fortunate to have excellent health care insurance provided by British Energy. I had been receiving physiotherapy and hydrotherapy for about a year at Carle Clinic where my doctor was situated. It was one of those moments when you just know that falling is inevitable. My first concern was for my back, hence, my wrist took the brunt of the fall. Never one to do anything by halves, I was in what felt like the middle of nowhere and my cell phone was in the car.

I had been walking on Constitution Trail. At certain times of the day this hard-surfaced trail was teeming with joggers, bikers, dog walkers and people on rollerblades. Part of it had been a disused railway so it was perfect, long and straight with trees and bushes either side. It was often used as an alternative transportation route for schools and local businesses, but it was ten in the morning and everyone was now where they were supposed to be for the day. The only sign of life was in a nearby trailer park. I had often heard locals refer to the people who lived there as 'trailer trash'. A lovely lady came to my rescue. She took me back to my car to allow me to fetch my phone. She insisted on taking a very bewildered Bracken into her car despite the fact she had her little boy with her who wasn't entirely sure about sharing the back seat with a large black dog. She consigned Bracken to the fenced off part of our back garden before taking me to hospital. She stayed until she knew I was being looked after. I had suggested calling an ambulance, but she seemed to think that a lot of insurance policies didn't cover that. I thought ours would, but I didn't want to risk it. I will be eternally grateful to that wonderful woman.

I ended up being taken to theatre to have pins, plates and a bone graft and spent three nights in hospital. I was terrified about the general anaesthesia, a throwback to my Seafield Hospital experience, but thankfully the anaesthetist was very understanding. I had got to know the physiotherapists in Carle Clinic quite well since I had been treated there every week for about a year, but it was still a lovely surprise when one of them came to visit me at home and brought a beautiful bouquet of yellow roses and a card signed by all of them. I was really touched, but soon found myself back in the department, this time to see an occupational therapist for my wrist.

I went back to visit my good Samaritan bearing gifts of thanks and gratitude. She explained that her husband had decided to return to university and that they sold their house to fund it. As the saying goes, never judge a book by its cover!

Figure 40: *Jemma's headshot from AMDA*

CHAPTER 22

LIVING NORMALLY

"Every moment wasted looking back, keeps us from moving forward."
- Hilary Clinton

Sightseeing was top of the agenda when we had visitors. Both sets of parents came to visit at least a couple of times during our stay. I enjoyed nothing better than climbing into the Jeep and heading to Chicago to act as a tour guide. I had been a nervous driver in Scotland, freaking out if I had to drive somewhere I had not been before. If anyone had told me that I would not only drive into Chicago and in fact all over Illinois and be more than happy to do so, no satnavs, remember, I would have told them they were deluded and possibly a bit mad. I also had a little quirky ritual, in that I would have the CD player set to play Frank Sinatra singing My Kind of Town, or Sweet Home Chicago from The Blues Brothers movie, just as we swept along Lake Shore Drive past the Shedd Aquarium on the right with the iconic Chicago skyline on the left. I loved the sight of Glorious Lake Michigan twinkling in the sunshine with yachts and boats nodding and dipping in the sparkling water as we approached Navy Pier, my preferred place to park. From Navy Pier, it was easy to either use the River Walk to get to the beautiful Wrigley Building, built by chewing gum tycoon William Wrigley Junior, on Michigan Avenue, or to take a water taxi along to the Shedd Aquarium.

Michigan Avenue was also known as the magnificent mile, and with good reason. It was a haven for shopping and architecture. I went on the architectural river boat tour with Mum and Dad. It was fascinating. For a start, it looked very familiar; I had become an avid ER fan when my back had left me housebound. I watched an episode every day for weeks. The neo-gothic Tribune Tower was particularly interesting to me. Home of the *Chicago Tribune* newspaper and Tribune Media, WGN radio. Colonel Robert McCormick brought a piece of rock from a medieval cathedral he had found to America during World War One. He asked news correspondents who worked for the *Chicago Tribune* to bring back similar fragments of rock and brickwork when they were travelling around the world. The accumulated fragments were incorporated into the lower levels of the building during its construction and labelled with the origin and location of the source for all to see. I was very pleased to see that as well as the Taj Mahal, Berlin Wall and the Great wall of China there was a piece of Edinburgh Castle rock. It felt strange to touch it being so very far away from home. There was even a piece of petrified wood from the Redwood National State Park. I read that a fragment of metal from the Twin Towers has been added.

I was at the top of the Sears Tower (now Willis Tower), all 1,450 feet of it, more times than I care to mention with various sets of visitors. The elevator ride to the top takes just sixty seconds, and if it is particularly windy in the city, the building is designed to sway which can be a bit disconcerting. No visit to Chicago was complete without a trip to Marshall Field's store on State Street. Marshall Field was an entrepreneur and his store became renowned for outstanding levels of customer service and exceptional quality. The store was used as a location in the film 'What Women Want' starring Mel Gibson and Helen Hunt. In 1887, Harry Gordon Selfridge became retail lead, and was at the helm of the flagship store as it developed into a modern department store. Selfridge resigned in 1904 and established his own rival store before heading to London to do the same.

The Loop is the business centre in Chicago and boasts many theatres and outdoor sculptures. The elevated train tracks are now iconic. There have been unsuccessful petitions in the past asking for them to be demolished and a subway installed. The tracks circle downtown Chicago and date back from the 19th century when Chicago was one of the fastest growing cities in the world. The great Chicago fire in 1871 had destroyed almost half the city, but the city re-invented itself and became the home of the original sky scraper and led the way in sky scraper design. The immense growth and development meant mass transportation of people in and around the city was required. Subways are expensive and time consuming to construct, it was more cost effective to build an elevated line and so the Chicago 'L' rapid transit system was born.

Shopping on the magnificent mile was amazing. I loved going into the Bloomingdale's building. My favourite shop in there was Williams and Sonoma who specialised in cooking utensils and cookware. Across the road from Bloomingdale's is the Water Tower shopping centre with a huge array of shops and eateries. On more than one occasion we would have enormous, juicy, chocolate-covered strawberries from Godiva, and delicious coffee from Gloria Jean's. The original Water Tower building is also located there. It was built in 1869 to house a giant water pump which was used to draw water from Lake Michigan. It was the only public building to survive the Great Chicago Fire, and is now used as a tourist information office. It is in this area of the city where you can hire a horse and carriage for a ride around downtown.

I had often wanted to buy popcorn from Garretts popcorn shop located further along Michigan Avenue; it had a vast variety of popcorn flavours, but there was always a queue outside stretching along the street. With so much to see, there never seemed to be enough time to stand in line. We would usually head back to Navy Pier to round off the day.

Navy Pier has a real holiday atmosphere – loads of entertainment, shops, restaurants, parks and gardens. It is a 3,300-foot-long structure which was designed by architect Charles Sumner Frost and opened in 1916 as The Municipal Pier. It was the only pier in America at that time which was used for shipping and public entertainment. Intriguingly, it had a prison to house draft dodgers during World War One.

It was re-named Navy Pier in 1927 to honour navy personnel who served during that war. During World War Two, the pier was used as a training centre for pilots, one of whom was George H. W. Bush.

At the end of the day, Navy Pier is a magical place to be as the lights in the buildings in the city begin to light up the amazing iconic skyline. Dinner cruise ships lined up along the pier; it was fascinating to watch people come and go. One of my favourite memories is of the four of us, OH Jemma and Lisa and I, sitting in a restaurant as dusk fell and the city lit up in front of our eyes for the first time.

During the day, there was no end of free family entertainment on offer – barber shop quartets, puppet shows, singing and dancing. The smell of roasting honeyed nuts seemed to fill the air and it was always decorated appropriately depending on the season; Halloween was my favourite. There was always so much to see, and it had a cheerful, relaxed atmosphere. Outside is the 150-foot Ferris Wheel which provides an excellent photo opportunity of Lake Shore Drive and the skyline. I can honestly say, Chicago with its outstanding architecture, history and charm is one of my favourite cities in the world.

Figure 41: *Bracken by the corn fields, Normal*

One of my favourite films of all time is 'It's A Wonderful Life' starring James Stewart and Donna Reed, set in the fictitious town of Bedford Falls. It was produced and directed by Frank Capra and was inspired by a book written by Philip Van Doren Stern, called *The Greatest Gift.* It is a bittersweet tale of a man who loses all hope just before Christmas. When I first clapped eyes on uptown Normal, I thought that the main street looked just like Bedford Falls. It is quaint, picturesque and oozes old-fashioned American charm. Imagine my absolute delight when I discovered that the restored art deco movie theatre in Normal had a tradition of showing the film every year in the run-up to Christmas. The theatre was built in 1937 and at that time was state of the art. It was closed in 1990 when the eight-screen Parkway cinema complex opened just off Veterans Parkway, the main thoroughfare between the Twin Cities. A community restoration began when the theatre was purchased by the town of Normal in 1993. It re-opened, fully restored to its former glory with plush new seating and lighting. It shows classic films throughout the year, as well as independent and foreign films.

Figure 42: *The movie theatre, Normal*

Going there to watch my favourite Christmas film was magical. There is no other word for it in my book. Inside the theatre, you could buy a paper cup filled with lemonade or cola. Popcorn was decanted by hand from giant bags. The seats had flip-up side tables to place your drink and popcorn on, and raffle tickets were sold to raise funds for the local community and charities. One year, Karolyn Grimes, the actress who had played Zu Zu, came to hand out the raffle prizes. Throughout the performance, the audience laughed, cried and applauded, although I am certain, most of them, like me, knew the script off by heart. Outside, idyllically, the street and shops were white with snow; it was almost like walking into the film. I will never forget that experience. Jemma came with me the first year, but when I wanted to go back the following year she firmly told Lisa, 'It's your turn.' I think they enjoyed it really.

Across the road from the theatre was Normal Post Office, and Normal Library wasn't far away. I never failed to smile if a police car drove past with 'Normal Police' written on it.

There was a small creek at the bottom of our garden. Dad in particular recalls the creek, because one time he was dog sitting, Bracken lay down in it and got completely covered with mud. Dad washed him with his own Pantene shampoo, rinsed and dried him and then Bracken promptly went and rolled in it again, bless him.

I have my own reasons for remembering the creek. It became necessary for me to drown a rabbit in it. I had noticed a rabbit on the lawn the night before this heart-rending incident, just sitting there, not moving, for quite some time. This was not a rare occurrence by any means. Rabbits and chipmunks would visit our garden daily, and happily sat around the ceramic dishes full of food I laid out for them in the enclosed part of the garden. I loved to watch them in the morning and in the evening, ever busy and munching the food greedily. The fireflies in the evenings were a beautiful sight too as they went hovering around the garden looking like ever-changing fairy lights. That night there was a dreadful thunder storm, but when I saw him just sitting there, I assumed the bunny would soon be hopping on his way to shelter. We did tend to get extreme weather, including tornadoes. There was a tornado siren just along from the house and no one had mentioned that it was tested on the first Tuesday of the month at ten in the morning. I got the fright of my life the first morning it went off, not to mention when it wailed for real on more than one occasion. It sounded spookily like a WWII air-raid siren and was unnerving. Strangely, Bracken always seemed to sense when it was about to go off and headed for the basement without being told to. I am sure there is some sort of explanation for this, but it never ceased to amaze me. When I awoke the next morning, the garden was almost completely flooded. I immediately noticed that the rabbit was still there.

I thought that it must be dead, but when I went to see, it was sporadically gasping for breath. I gently turned it over I saw straightaway that it had a large, red, raw puncture wound in its side I thought it looked like a gunshot wound, but not having seen one before, I wasn't sure.

I couldn't face doing anything physically violent to put the poor thing out of its misery, but to leave it to die a slow lingering death was unconceivable. With tears pouring down my face I took the rabbit to the bottom of the garden and placed it in the deepest part of the water I could find and put him in; he seemed to be gazing at me with misty faraway eyes. I couldn't bear to watch its life ebb away. When I eventually did look through my fingers, the poor little thing was gone. I cried off and on for the rest of the day (and the next) about that little rabbit.

I also came to the rescue of one of my feathered friends. I had numerous bird feeders in the garden. One black bird who had red and yellow circles on his wings, would shrill loudly if the food ran out as if to say, 'Come on, we need a refill.' We also saw the occasional northern cardinal, or 'Red Bird', the Illinois State emblem and name of the local football team. I even saw a humming bird one day – it was so fragile, exquisitely tiny and pretty.

I noticed a bird hopping and flapping frantically about at the bottom of the garden. It seemed to be trying to fly but it couldn't take off. On closer inspection, I found that it was indeed trying to fly, but that it had a small dead bird attached to one of its legs with twine of some sort. I went back inside to fetch a pair of scissors; I knew what had to be done. I cut off the dead bird's leg, the one attached to the other bird with the twine. I tried to do this with my eyes shut but was scared in case I cut off the wrong one, or worse still, harmed the bird who was alive. Everything went well, and the newly freed bird soared up into the sky, good deed done.

Although I try to love all creatures great and small, even spiders – I will not kill one, I will admit to a phobia when it comes to snakes. I remember trying to set an example and be brave in front of Jemma and Lisa at Edinburgh Zoo. There was a 'touch' table with a snake skin on it amongst various other animal-related things. I really didn't want to pass my phobia to them, but I just couldn't bring myself to go anywhere near it or watch when they touched the discarded skin. Sad but true.

I also discovered we had a large green praying mantis in the back garden. I found this creature to be fascinating; its little green head seemed to follow me around the garden, cartoon like, cautiously watching my every move. I even found it on one of our kitchen chairs one day.

Not long after we moved in to the house in Ironwood, I saw what I thought was a piece of black rubber on the pavement outside the garage door. Dad and OH were there and they rather too quickly assured me that was exactly what it was, and I thought no more about it.

Sometime later, I was in the back-garden throwing Bracken's favourite toy; it was a huge rubber dumbbell attached to a rope, I could throw it quite a distance. It was affectionately referred to simply as 'Toy'.

As Bracken ran to the bottom of the garden to fetch Toy, out of the corner of my right eye, I saw a thin black snake head rise up through the grass. It had yellow stripes on it, and then another did the same as if to say, 'Hey, who is disturbing the peace around here?' My legs turned to jelly and I got a metallic taste in my mouth and felt as if I was frozen to the spot. I screamed at Bracken to 'come here now' and then went running into the house like a thing possessed, swiftly closing the door behind me. I stood, breathlessly leaning against the patio door trying to regain some sense of composure. I called OH; quite what I thought he would or could do about it while he was at work, I don't know, but it seemed important to share my experience. As usual, I reached his answering machine, but I left a message hoping that no one else would be able to hear his hysterical wife rambling on about snakes in the grass.

A friend of Jemma's thought he could help me by bringing me a snake skin. He had just watched the snake shed it in our garden. He truly thought that if he could show it to me and let me touch it, that I would get over my so-called phobia. I was in the basement at the time working on the computer. There was only one way out, and that path was blocked by some idiot holding a snake skin! I suffered quite badly with migraines at that time, and boy did I have a doozy after that episode.

Our first Thanksgiving was enjoyable. We had invited friends, Kevin and Sue and their two children, and I attempted traditional American thanksgiving fare. The only thing which spoiled it was the thought of doing the whole turkey dinner thing again the following month. As luck would have it, the day after Thanksgiving, celebrated on the fourth Thursday of November, it started to snow. The day after Thanksgiving is called Black Friday because that is when Americans go out looking for bargains, a bit like our Boxing Day sales. Why we have introduced Black Friday to the UK I will never understand. However, I digress yet again. It was soft fluffy snow. It nestled on tree branches and softly covered roads and pavements. It was still snowing in December. I was beside myself, a real-life white Christmas. I threw myself into all American Christmas traditions, namely making eggnog, decorating the house inside and out, gift making and giving, and fundraising. I loved to drive around Ironwood at night just to look at the houses liberally decorated with coloured lights. I had always loved the film 'National Lampoon's Christmas Vacation', and now I felt like I was living on the set. The school held concerts and encouraged parents to buy poinsettias to raise money for charity. The plants were used to decorate the stage before being claimed and taken home by the owners. They made a beautiful Christmassy floral display for the audience to enjoy and savour as well as listening to the students perform festive music.

Driveways were cleared with snow blowers. Icicles, large and small, were dripping, diamond like, from fences and trees. Hats and gloves were donned, nostril hair froze, and automatic garage doors once scorned by me, really did seem to be necessary. Driving became difficult to say the least, but never was a drama turned into a crisis. This was just a way of life and everyone took it in their stride. I bought Bracken snow boots to stop his paws from icing up in the extreme cold weather. He was less than impressed, displaying what looked like indignity while wearing them, and looked like something from Monty Python's Ministry of Silly Walks as he pranced around the garden trying to get them off again! Jemma and I took him for a walk after what seemed like weeks being cooped up indoors waiting for cabin fever to set in. His whiskers froze completely and looked like frosted white spikes. We did learn never to underestimate the weather in Illinois, hot or cold. By March, the snow and ice were becoming a bit tiresome. But spring seemed to materialise very suddenly, and people went from wearing heavy coats and boots, to wearing shorts and sandals almost overnight.

*

When she was in her senior year at NWCHS, Jemma auditioned for a place at the American Musical and Dramatic Academy, AMDA, in New York. The auditions were held in the Chicago Hilton and

Towers, 720 S. Michigan Avenue. I was impressed by the atmosphere and general organisation, especially when the would-be students were told not to expect an apartment like the one used in the sitcom 'Friends', and that the reality of living in Manhattan would be somewhat different to that television programme. A few weeks later Jemma received a letter from AMDA telling her she had been accepted. It was thrilling news; we were delighted although baulked at the cost. Then reality set in. Our eighteen-year-old daughter would be moving, alone, to New York City for at least two years. The drive from our house to Midway Airport took about two hours, the flight from Midway to La Guardia took two hours and twenty minutes. She would even be in a different time zone – Illinois is in the Central time zone, Manhattan is in the Eastern time zone, an hour's difference.

When the time came for her to move into her student accommodation we drove to New York with the Jeep packed floor to ceiling with her things. Little did we realise that her accommodation wasn't much bigger than the Jeep. Her accommodation at that time was in the Greystone Building 212 W 91st and Broadway. Her room was up several flights of wooden stairs, there was no lift. I found myself anxiously looking around for smoke detectors and fire escapes. The room had a linoleum floor, bunk beds, a chunky old-fashioned radiator, and a couple of bits of furniture for storage of clothes etc. The shared bathroom was next door and although it was clean it was shabby but most definitely not chic. The drive into the city had been sombre. Just one month before, the Twin Towers had been attacked and totally destroyed on 9/11, changing the New York skyline forever. The whole world had been shocked and baffled by the atrocity and I cannot find the words to describe the effect it had on us.

On the morning of the 11th of September, I had been in the basement checking emails. I had been watching 'Good Morning America' before going to the basement and had left the television switched on to that news channel. After checking my emails, I climbed the basement steps and entered the sitting room. I looked at the screen, listened to the commentary, and realised something life changing was happening before my eyes. Lisa was in bed, she had a throat infection and had the day off school. I called her down to watch, aware that the overwhelming, life-shattering scenes were history in the making. Jemma was babysitting; she was helping out an anaesthetist and his wife looking after their boys in the mornings, giving them breakfast, getting them ready for and taking them to school. I called her cell phone and told her to come straight home as soon as she was finished. OH called and told me to stay at home with the girls; we were ex-pats – he worked in a nuclear establishment and at that time no one knew exactly what was going on or why. The rest of the day was spent glued to the television screen, staring at it in disbelief as the traumatising scenes unfolded. The school was closed for the day, and one by one, we ended up with many of Jemma and Lisa's friends in our sitting room, to this day I am not sure why, but it was comforting to have them with us.

During my first visit to New York City, the towers had stood proud and tall, like twin sentries on duty. Now the skyline looked unguarded and bereft. There was a strong military presence, and people looked weary and grim. I just could not believe that I was going to leave Jemma in that broken city, all alone. I am not ashamed to say that I cried all the way home. The journey took thirteen hours and twenty-seven minutes.

For many months, I could not go into Jemma's room without crying. I realise now that her going was the final straw. I was homesick, my marriage was not a happy one and had caused much heartache, and I was terribly lonely. When I went to the school to watch Lisa in a play or concert, I found that if one of the other mothers asked me how Jemma was doing I would burst into tears. I will admit here and now, it was one of the most miserable and unhappy times of my life.

Jemma eventually settled in, but it took longer than expected; only she can truly say how she felt at that time, but I sensed that she was unhappy. I went to visit as often as I could and grew to love the city, especially the upper west side where she lived. I watched the film 'You've Got Mail' starring Tom Hanks and Meg Ryan many times because it was filmed there. Watching the film, I could see the Starbucks she walked past every day, and Zabars delicatessen and grocery store where I would buy her treats before heading back to Normal. Lisa and I went just before Christmas and the three of us went to see 'Beauty and the Beast' on Broadway. It was enchanting, a fairy tale brought to life with vibrancy and colour on stage. The city was gradually coming back to life; human spirits were recovering and refusing to let terrorism win. We watched skaters in Central Park and went to see the Christmas display in Macy's window.

I am, however, slightly ashamed to say that no matter how hard I tried, I cried every time Jemma went back to NYC after a visit home or when I was returning home after a visit to NYC.

Figure 43: *Me and Dad, Death Valley*

Figure 44: *Mum and Dad at the Grand Canyon*

CHAPTER 23

IT'S GREAT TO GO TRAVELLING

"A woman is like a teabag, only in hot water do you realise how strong she is."
- Nancy Reagan

We were very fortunate to visit many beautiful and interesting places while we were living in the States.

New Orleans was a fascinating place. I particularly enjoyed the French Quarter with its ornate ironwork galleries and balconies. Bourbon Street was alive with the sound of live jazz bands, Dixieland and Ragtime music. It was in Bourbon Street where I tried alligator sausages for the first (and last) time. It tasted just like chicken!

We visited the unusual and beautiful Lafayette Cemetery No. 1. I had hoped, rather selfishly although not uncaringly that there might have been a funeral the day we went to visit having seen the amazing spectacle of a New Orleans funeral on television and in films. I was mesmerised by the paddlewheel steamboats as they majestically sailed along the Mississippi. A good vantage point is Toulouse Street Wharf. The unique sound of the all-American Steam Calliope, a thirty-two-note steam pipe organ drifting on the breeze as they passed by. We were fortunate enough to take a trip on the *Natchez* and discovered just how loud the music was when you are situated next to the pipes as steam plumes emanated with each whistle toot.

We went to Memphis for a long weekend but only managed to scratch the surface of all the attractions there. Graceland's mansion, former home of Elvis Presley, was exciting and interesting. As well as the house and gardens, we walked through Elvis's customised jet the *Lisa Marie* complete with its gold-plated seatbelt buckles. Beale Street was fascinating and buzzing with activity. The street runs from the Mississippi River to East Street. It consists of 1.8 miles of blues clubs and restaurants. Walking along Beale Street is a real treat for the auditory and olfactory nerves. Pulled pork and BBQ aromas ooze from every nook and cranny. Live music permeates the atmosphere and it is easy to imagine seeing the likes of Louis Armstrong, Muddy Waters and BB King moseying along it. It was declared Home of the Blues by an Act of Congress. As the saying goes, the beer was cold and the music was hot, perfect. We stayed at the Peabody Hotel in Memphis, famous for its daily duck march. The hotel is beautiful and has a stunning fountain in the magnificent lobby, but it is famous for the ducks who march to the fountain in the morning and then back up to their duck palace on the roof in the evening. The ducks have even appeared on Sesame Street when Bert and Ernie celebrated rubber ducky day, and they have been on the Oprah Winfrey show. I must mention that the ducks are never domesticated or treated like pets and they only do a three-month stint before being retiring to their natural habitat. Also, you will never ever find duck on the restaurant menu! Apparently, the duck tradition began in the 1930s when the General Manager Frank Schutt came back from a hunting weekend a bit worse for wear and thought it would be funny to put his (then legal) live duck decoys in the fountain and they were a big hit. Prior to this apparently baby alligators and turtles had been placed in the fountain, hopefully not at the same time. In 1940, Bellman Edward Penbrook, who had been a circus animal trainer in a previous life, offered to help get the ducks to and from the fountain every day and taught them the now famous duck march. He retired in 1991 after fifty years' duck service. What a fantastic way to earn a living.

The return journey from Memphis was highly entertaining in that Jemma was helping Lisa to learn her lines for the school production of 'Fiddler on the Roof'. Lisa was playing the part of Zeitle. They were obviously getting a bit bored so decided to rehearse in the style of Terence and Philip from South Park. It was hilarious, both girls are excellent mimics. When I went to see the production, it was very hard to keep a straight face as I remembered the more unconventional version on that journey home.

*

Mum and Dad flew out to look after Bracken for the three weeks while we went to California. Dad dropped us off at Midway Airport in Chicago. I was so worried; just as he left an almighty thunder and lightning storm brewed. The sky turned black, lightning bolts zig-zagged across it. The rain was torrential, bouncing off the airport roof, but he managed to drive back to Normal safely and thankfully, it had passed by the time we were due to take off.

He and Mum had a lovely time while we were away by all accounts, they especially loved going to Barnes and Noble book shop just off Veterans Parkway on Empire, which was open until nine at night, ten on Fridays and Saturdays. Mum loves books, so they spent many hours there browsing, drinking coffee and enjoying cake in the comfy sofas and armchairs which were dotted around the shop. They also loved taking trips to Wal-Mart which was open twenty-four hours a day.

I think it was because they were getting a real sense of living in America and not just a tourist experience. One of their favourite pastimes was to watch the trains come and go at Normal railway station. Dad would film them and record the distinctive howl and wail as the trains screeched through the station.

It gives me a warm glow to think that they got to visit a great portion of America, including Las Vegas, the Grand Canyon, Hoover Dam, Death Valley, St Louis, although Mum would have preferred not to go up the arch, New York and of course Chicago.

While they were in New York they went to see 42nd Street on 42nd Street, went up the Empire State Building, and got to see the Amsterdam Building on west 85th where Jemma was living. They also managed a tour of the historic Ansonia Building (where Ziegfeld once lived) which is located on 2109 Broadway, west 73rd Street where Jemma had many of her classes. We went to Café Lalo on 201 West 83rd Street, where Meg Ryan and Tom Hanks filmed a scene from You've Got Mail, they even sat at the same table as Tom and Meg! They also got their photograph taken with a genuine New York cop.

The most poignant part of the New York visit for my parents was undoubtedly visiting Ground Zero. It was a truly heartbreaking but touching sight. I will never forget the messages and flowers that had been left there, and the dust filling the atmosphere setting the tone, as bulldozers and trucks worked to clear the area.

*

From Midway Airport (remember our trip?) we flew to San Francisco International Airport where we picked up our hire car which was to take us on our three-week grand tour of the state. Jemma's friend Lauren was working in San Francisco at that time, her parents Nicola and Geoff were in San Francisco to visit her, so we had the opportunity to meet up and catch up which was wonderful.

Yosemite National Park was simply stunning. It is in the Sierra Nevada mountains and is awash with waterfalls, alpine meadows and giant sequoia trees. The air was so crisp and clean, and the sunlight seemed to bounce out from every granite monolith, bathing the whole area with a creamy buttery light. It was interesting to learn that John Muir, a Scottish naturalist, had built and lived in a log cabin by Yosemite creek. John Muir Country Park in Dunbar had been a favourite place for us to visit when we lived in North Berwick. Bracken in particular loved leaping through the long grasses like a gazelle and swimming in the clear water there. John Muir was born in Dunbar, East Lothian in 1838. His family emigrated to America in 1849, but he never forgot his Scottish roots and was known to be an admirer of Robert Burns. Muir was said to have been 'overwhelmed' by the Yosemite landscape and I can't say I blame him. One part of our visit there was slightly tainted in that a hotel we went into one day, immediately struck me as being just like the fictional Overlook Hotel used in the film 'The Shining' starring Jack Nicholson. I remember going to see the film in the cinema when it first came out and was terrified by it. Years later when we had moved to North Berwick it was on television and I thought I was brave enough to watch it, but I got too scared. I asked OH if he would come upstairs with me and wait until I got into bed. When I came out of the bathroom after brushing my teeth, I found an envelope pinned to our bedroom door saying Room 237 and my husband laughing and saying, 'Here's Johnny!' inside. I won't tell you what I called him that night. Interestingly, the room number in the book is 217, but the management of the Timberline Hotel in Colorado, where the exterior shots of the hotel were filmed, asked if it could be changed so that guests wouldn't avoid room 217. Sensible idea if you ask me. That incident also reminds me of another film and another prank . Shortly before we moved to America, we decorated our dining room. We chose a Lindsay tartan carpet which was maroon and green, (to tie in with the blue/green Blackwatch tartan hall and stair carpet we had fitted) and painted the walls a rich merlot. It looked lovely, especially after we had renovated the fireplace using slate and marble removing all signs of previous owners attempts at modernisation. The ceiling was quite high, and we had been using a paint roller with a long extension pole.

Mags and I had taken Jemma and her friend Sarah to see the 25th anniversary showing of 'The Exorcist 'at the cinema. Jemma and Sarah were taking part in' Godspell' which was being performed by North Berwick high school drama group at the Edinburgh Fringe Festival, (more major fundraising!) Jemma had a solo part and so had opted out of a trip to Russia with her father and Lisa.(several similar trips were planned by British Energy to and from Russia around that time as gestures of goodwill following on from Chernobyl) We could only get into the late showing and I will admit that I fell asleep and so have yet to see it.

Eventually the film was released on DVD and again with some persuasion, we rented it for Jemma, Lisa, Sarah and Simon, Jemma's boyfriend. They settled in to watch the movie with popcorn, sweets etc, dimmed lights and closed curtains. You might remember that the sitting room had turret windows? Well, this meant that the extension pole could easily be pushed through the open dining room window and reach the sitting room window. Remember that this was three floors up from the ground. Apparently, Bracken had heard something and had walked towards the window whilst emitting a low and steady growl, hackles rising as he went, which had caused quite a bit of discomposure amongst the captive audience. I can only imagine their facial expressions when they heard tapping at the window!

We toured Napa Valley and stopped in the historic city of Calistoga. The scenery was breathtaking; row upon row of vineyards nestling into the hillsides basking in the sun. Of course, we got to sample some prized Cabernet Sauvignon in a few of Napa Valley's four hundred wineries and excellent restaurants.

We spent some time in Las Vegas. It was a great experience, especially staying in the Bellagio Hotel and watching the famous water fountains. That was where Jemma and Lisa decided to call room service for some strawberries. The huge, fragrant, luscious berries arrived in their very own handmade chocolate basket. I am pleased to report that I have now forgotten how much we were charged for them. We then headed to Death Valley, passing by the Hoover Dam. We were to re-visit these locations again with Mum and Dad, but I will never forget my first visit to Death Valley. I was totally mesmerised by it and its stories of covered wagon trains and the 49ers.

The 49ers were pioneers who made their way to Sutters Mill, California when gold was discovered there in 1848. The biggest influx began in 1849, hence the name. People from all over America and some from further afield undertook the onerous journey, mostly overland, across the mountains setting up mining camps as they went. These camps had everything you could imagine – shops, saloons, banks, even brothels and of course lawlessness.

On the 16th of April 1846, the now infamous Donner-Reed party set off from Springfield Illinois seeking adventure and of course fortune in the form of gold. The instigator had been James Frasier Reed. James took along his wife Margaret, and their four children, twelve-year-old Virginia, Patty, James and Thomas and his mother-in-law. Reed, who was a successful businessman in Illinois, had an elaborate, two-storey wagon made for his family so that they could travel in relative style and comfort. The wagon had spring-cushioned seats, sleeping bunks and even an iron stove. It was so heavy that it took eight oxen to pull it. Virginia called it 'The Pioneer Palace Car'.

The group, consisting of nine wagons was led by brothers George Donner, a sixty-two-year-old farmer who had eventually settled in Springfield after moving around the country several times, and his equally adventurous brother Jacob.

After six gruelling months crossing arduous terrain, tempers were beginning to fray at the edges. On the 5th of October, two wagons became tangled up, and a driver called John Snyder started to whip his oxen as punishment for the collision. James Reed was furious about the cruel treatment being meted out and demanded that John should stop beating the unfortunate animals. John did not stop. James Reed reacted by grasping for his knife and stabbed John in the stomach, killing him.

The party promptly dispensed their own form of justice. Although some thought James should hang, in the end, the party voted to banish James.

Reed was last seen leaving his family and the rest of the party riding off with a man called Walter Herron. I feel another bit of family research coming on!

"My father, with tears in his eyes, tried to smile as one friend after another grasped his hand in a last farewell. Mama was overcome with grief. At last we were all in the wagons. The drivers cracked their whips. The oxen moved slowly forward, and the long journey had begun."

- Virginia Reed

While they were crossing the rough terrain of the Sierra Nevada mountain range, one wagon suffered a broken axel. The party decided to set up camp for the night to repair it. That night saw a snowfall of more than five feet. There were drifts up to sixty feet high; in short, it was one of the most brutal and fierce winters on record. The party became trapped. Of the eighty-one people stranded at Truckee Lake, more than half were under the age of eighteen, six were mere infants. Within three weeks of being trapped their food supply had been used up. The decision was made to kill their pack animals and dogs for food. They ended up resorting to eating dirt and twigs, tree bark and boiled leather.

Reluctantly, the decision was made to resort to cannibalism. One person would be sacrificed in order for the others to survive. They thought of drawing lots or even having a duel to decide who should be slain, but all too soon, some of the party died of natural causes. On Christmas Day 1846 they ate their first human, carefully labelling the flesh so that no one would eat their own kith and kin. Both George and Jacob Donner, their wives and children perished before rescue came some five months later.

In all forty-one people died, forty-six survived; many of the survivors lost toes because of frostbite.

The Donner Pass is now known as The Lincoln Highway.

We stayed in the Furnace Creek Inn while we were in Death Valley. We were there in late June, when it is common for temperatures to reach forty-nine degrees centigrade (120°F) and only dipping to thirty-two degrees centigrade during the night. There is less than two inches of rainfall annually. It was dark by the time we reached the inn, we seemed to drive through mile after mile of desert with no sign of life. I must admit I was beginning to panic a bit and breathed a huge sigh of relief when we eventually saw lights in the distance and signs of civilization. The air conditioning in the car was going flat out so we were nice and cool, but the windows were hot to touch, it was a very odd experience. We visited the ranch and the Borax Museum. There was an eighteen-hole golf course, the lowest elevation course in the world, and of course we went to Badwater Basin, the lowest point of North America at 280 feet below sea level (Dad and I got our photograph taken there when we went back again for another visit).

Furnace Creek is only 120 miles north west of Las Vegas, but it truly is like another world. It is almost surreal, and I fell in love with it, even when we got a puncture in the middle of the day at Zabriskie Point!

About thirty-five miles from Furnace Creek in the Bullfrog hills, near the Bullfrog gold mine, is Rhyolite, one of the largest ghost towns in the area. The boomtown, which sprang up after prospectors found high-grade ore nearby in 1905, had a population of about ten to twelve thousand people at its peak in 1907. It was served by three railroads, forty-five saloons, an opera house, a slaughterhouse, a hospital, a three-storey bank and a school. It even had three public swimming pools. The town was affected financially by the San Francisco earthquake in 1906, and financial panic started in 1907. The mines were not yielding ore any longer, causing businesses to close, and residents to leave in droves. Only ruins of the original buildings remain, plus one building constructed from thousands of beer, whisky and wine bottles which had been in plentiful supply during the town's heyday. We met a very pleasant couple who acted as caretakers for the building. They lived in a caravan; I still don't know how they managed to live there, but they seemed happy enough.

We didn't go to Scotty's Castle on that occasion, but when we returned with Mum and Dad we managed a visit. It really is the most curious sight, a two-storey Spanish-style mansion forty-five miles north of Stovepipe Wells. It has turrets in the front which presumably gave it the title Castle. Inside it is furnished with custom-made furniture imported from Europe, hand-wrought iron implements, imported tiles and it even has a 1,121-pipe organ! It was the epitome of style to spend time there and was frequented by Hollywood stars in the 1920s and 30s.

Scotty, himself, was a con man who sold shares to a fictional gold mine. Walter Scott, who became known as 'Death Valley Scotty' was born in 1872. He joined Buffalo Bill's Wild West Show in 1890; he was a showman as well as a con man.

He had convinced a Chicago millionaire, Albert Mussey Johnson, to invest. Johnson found out that Scotty's claims about the goldmine were fraudulent, but curiously, the two men became friends. Construction of the mansion which was to be branded as Scotty's Castle, began in 1922. Albert Mussey Johnson's wife Bessie wanted somewhere secure and relaxing to reside when she was in Grapevine Canyon, a place she came to love. She is quoted as saying, 'Moonlight anywhere is a delight. But there's no moonlight in the world that can compare with the moonlight in Grapevine Canyon, our desert canyon, where the castle stands.'

The stock market crash in 1929 made it difficult to finish construction, so Mr. Johnson decided to let rooms to raise money. It became a popular destination for the rich and famous in the roaring 20s.

Mr. and Mrs. Johnson died without having children and therefore left the castle to a charity which Mr. Johnson had founded in 1946. In 1970 the property was bought by the National Park Services.

Scotty died in 1954 having lived in the castle for two years being looked after by the charity and is buried beside his cherished dog on a hill which overlooks the castle.

Walter Scott Rangers dressed in 1930s-style uniforms conduct tours of this remarkable and astonishing castle. I am so glad we were able to visit and take a tour.

*

Our Californian adventure took us to Los Angeles, where we did all the usual touristy things like driving along Rodeo Drive and going up to the iconic Hollywood sign. We also went to Disneyland and Universal Studios. I was careful about which rides to go on, however, after an unpredicted experience at Disney World in Florida. I had been persuaded by the girls to go on the Rock 'n' Roller Coaster which was a series of loops and dips in the dark accompanied by very loud Aerosmith music. I enjoyed it – well, kind of – and so allowed myself to be persuaded to go into The Tower of Terror. Big mistake.

In true Disney style, you enter 'The Hollywood Tower Hotel' via a pathway through the extremely atmospheric and overgrown grounds. The whole effect created to look like the hotel closed abruptly many years ago and has been left untouched ever since. Creepy-looking bellhops inform you that your room is not ready – they were very good actors – and you are asked to wait in the hotel library. So far so good, except that 1930s music played the whole time and it reminded me so much of The Shining that I was quaking in my sandals before we even got into the elevator. The effects were amazing, and my overactive imagination told me I really was in an old haunted hotel. Thunder and lightning could be heard and seen, and then with an almighty crash of thunder the power went out, leaving a small, very old-fashioned television crackling in the corner playing the theme to the Twilight Zone. Apologies if this is not entirely accurate, by this time I was ready for a lie down. We were then ushered into an elevator, and I felt sick. They say you never get the same terror experience twice, they alter the pattern of the ride each time, but basically, you go up, drop down enough to frighten the life out of you as the doors open to reveal a long dimly lit hotel corridor complete with ghostly apparitions, before being taken up to the top where the doors open again to reveal the sunlit park 199 feet below. Then, just when I thought it couldn't get any worse, you plummet towards the ground, but not at free-fall speed, oh no, they create a weightless effect by attaching cables to the bottom which pull the elevator at a speed slightly faster than a free fall, 39 miles per hour. When you get out, there is the 1930s Shining type of music again and a voice says, *'A warm welcome back to those of you who made it, and a friendly word of warning, something you won't find in any guidebook. The next time you check into a deserted hotel on the dark side of Hollywood, make sure you know just what kind of vacancy you're filling. Or you may find yourself a permanent resident... of the Twilight Zone'*

It was the last straw. I thought I might benefit from a large glass of wine, either that, or I was about to have a migraine. In the end, I had both!

Now, staying on the *Queen Mary* was, by far much more my cup of tea, but not dissimilar in many ways. I absolutely loved it.

CHAPTER 24

RMS QUEEN MARY

"How inappropriate to call this planet Earth when it is clearly Ocean."
- Arthur C. Clarke

We were fortunate enough to stay on board the *Queen Mary* Hotel for three nights. During the day, tourists came on board to tour the ship but only hotel guests were allowed on board at night, that was when my imagination went into overdrive as I thought about the ship's history and famous passengers.

The atmosphere changed dramatically at night; it was much quieter, and I loved wandering around the promenade deck and sun deck imagining all the people who had crossed the Atlantic on the ship, especially the rich and famous. Bob Hope was on the final passage before World War Two (WW2) brought passenger crossings to a halt. Bing Crosby crossed the Atlantic several times on board including with the United Service Organization, USO, which was developed in 1941 to boost the morale of troops overseas.

Elizabeth Taylor crossed the Atlantic with her beloved poodles; the kennels for all pampered pooches at that time were situated on the sports deck. Other Hollywood film-star passengers include Audrey Hepburn, Cary Grant and Clark Gable.

Lynn Redgrave was on board during the very last voyage in 1967. Dignitaries who have travelled on board this magnificent ship include the Queen Mother, Winston Churchill and President Eisenhower.

In 1839, the British government and Cunard developed a contract to deliver mail to and from America. Reliable, fast ships were necessary for that vital service.

Plans to build the *Queen Mary* began in 1926, but the Great Depression of 1927 placed a spanner firmly in the works. The British government decided to give a loan to Cunard to allow them to complete building the ship, but only if they agreed to merge with their competitors, the White Star Line (who had built *Titanic*).

The RMS *Queen Mary* crossed the Atlantic one thousand and one times after she was launched from John Brown shipyard in Clydebank, Glasgow. Up until the day of the launch, on the 26th of September 1934, she had been known simply as *job number 534*. On that pouring wet September day, Queen Mary, accompanied by King George V, announced for the first time that the new liner was to be named *Queen Mary*. Loud cheers and cries of delight echoed around the shipyard as the newly named ship slid into the especially widened River Clyde.

The liner became the epitome of elegance, comfort and style, and was known as 'The Ship of Beautiful Woods' She was also extremely fast, in fact, her speed was used as a weapon during WW2; she was faster than the torpedoes which were fired by German U-boats. Hitler offered a reward of $25,000 and the Iron Cross, to any U-boat captain who could sink her.

The *Queen Mary* became a Government Service Transport ship during the war and was used to transport American GIs. across the Atlantic Ocean to Britain.

GI stood for 'Government Issue' and was stamped on army equipment. Eventually the term GI became used as an abbreviation for American troops. It has been said that many soldiers used the abbreviation with more than a touch of sarcasm, believing that they were nothing more than mass-produced products to be issued by the United States government.

The soldiers used a warm bunking system, using bunks for eight hours at a time; the bunks never had time to grow cold. The great ship was painted grey and was known as 'The Grey Ghost'. She usually crossed without an escort, but on the second of October 1942, she was escorted by His Majesty's ship, HMS *Curacoa* who provided an anti-aircraft escort for the last part of her journey to Greenock from New York. The *Queen Mary* had been following an indirect zig-zag course at that time, which was meant to confuse German submarines, known as U-boats. The HMS *Curacoa* was also following a zig-zag course. It not known exactly what happened, but the two ships found themselves in a collision course – each captain thought the other would take evasive action. The ships collided. The *Queen Mary* split the smaller ship in two, one witness later said it was like 'a knife through butter', and almost immediately, the smaller ship was engulfed in flames. The HMS *Curacoa* sank within six minutes; 338 men perished from a crew of 439. The *Queen Mary* was following strict orders not to stop for anything in the U-boat-infested waters and continued to Scotland with her now damaged bow. The 15,000 GIs on board felt helpless as they threw life jackets and life belts to the men drowning in the sea. The men who witnessed the tragic accident were sworn to secrecy and the loss was not made public until the war was over for fear of demoralising the nation. After a lengthy trial blame was apportioned as two thirds the fault of the *Curacoa*, one third the *Queen Mary*.

In 1943, The Grey Ghost carried sixteen thousand, six hundred and eighty-three men, the largest number of humans ever carried in one vessel. At the end of the war the ship was used to carry American soldiers back to their homeland, along with over thirty thousand war brides and babies. I have seen photographs of some war brides on board. The women, some very young, looked happy and excited. I often wonder what they were really thinking. I suppose when we are young everything is an adventure and you either don't foresee pitfalls or choose not to. I remember watching one lady being interviewed many years later. She explained that she had never seen her husband out of uniform before, and that although they had been married for almost three years, she barely recognised him. I only know that my own experience of arriving in the States, living so far away from friends and family was not easy, and I had the benefit of British Airways, the telephone and the internet to fall back on. I know I cannot and should not try to compare my experience in the year 2000 with these courageous men and women in the 1940s, but I do understand what it feels like not to recognise someone you are married to.

At the end of the war, the ship was re-fitted for civilian trans-

Atlantic service and was fully restored to her former glory, complete with her beautiful wood panelling and inlays, including American and French walnut, British and Australian oak and ash. Fifty types of wood were used, plus fifty-six polished veneers, one for each of the British colonies at the time the ship was built. Six of those woods are now extinct and the *Queen Mary* is one of the few places where they can be seen. The ship is full of intricate carvings and decorative murals. Copious amounts of glass and marble were used to decorate her, as well as the ultra-modern and fashionable, at that time, linoleum which was used in the main foyer, the social and shopping area for cabin (first) class passengers. Indian Silverwood furnished the walls inlaid with Indian laurel bands. The tobacco shop was constructed using cedar wood from Honduras.

There were three classes of passenger on board, and three separate entrances. Cabin, tourist (second) and third class. Cunard proudly claimed that third class on the *Queen Mary* was the equivalent to first-class travel on other ships, but I am not certain that was true.

Cabin-class passenger cabins were situated in the centre of the ship, top to bottom because this was where they could be offered the smoothest crossing. Tourist class were located aft at the stern (the rear of the ship) top to bottom, and third-class passengers at the bow top to bottom. During rough weather, the bow was known to completely disappear under crashing waves.

In its heyday, the Verandah Grill was the most popular night-time destination on board the *Queen Mary*. It was twenty-nine feet wide, and seventy feet long, and boasted a semi-circular glazed wall which looked out onto the sun deck. It was, and still is, a sight to behold. Cabin-class passengers had to reserve a table to dine there. It was used as a dining room, supper club and cocktail bar and offered an *à la carte* menu. The dance floor was made from sycamore parquet with a mahogany border. It also had a pearwood inlay and a band of ebonised hornbeam. The stage, used by the dance band, was in front of a 1,000-foot square mural which was painted by Scottish artist Doris Zinkeisen. (Doris was re-commissioned to oversee the refurbishment of it after the war and is thought to have been so very unhappy about the damage caused to her painstakingly created mural, that she left a mouse painted into the hair of Marie Antoinette.) Glass dividers which were used as railings between the levels, changed colour in time to the music, and reflectors helped to illuminate cabin-class passengers twirling and swaying feet. The rest of the grill was fitted with a self-coloured black Wilton carpet which was insisted upon by Doris. What a magnificent and decadent sight it must have been on the primarily art-deco-styled ship, but it was strictly for cabin-class passengers only.

The cabin-class dining room was the largest ever built at that time. It was three decks high and spanned the entire width, 118 feet, of the ship. It had private dining rooms in each corner and in its entirety, could accommodate all 815 cabin-class passengers in one sitting should it ever be required.

On two occasions, the restaurant was unable to provide what a passenger requested. One request was for Dr Pepper which was not available in the UK at that time; the steward thought it was some sort of health drink but knew he didn't have it on board the ship. The other was when some oil tycoons asked for rattlesnake steaks. Apparently, the passengers who requested this unusual dish were given baked eel while waiters waved baby rattles as a joke. Ugh!

The cabin-class swimming pool was on 'D' deck below the main foyer. It boasted a vaulted ceiling which was covered with simulated mother of pearl. The actual pool was tiled with beige-coloured terracotta tiles which were decorated with bands of green. It was fully enclosed and so could be enjoyed all year round. It is thought to be haunted. Many people have visited and taken the *Queen Mary* ghost tour. The pool balcony led through revolving doors to the Turkish bath suite, which was divided into the classical laconicum, caldarium, tepidarium and frigidarium for heating, cooling and cleansing the body. It also sported a steam room and massage room. Ingeniously, the terracotta tiles grew darker as you left the pool area to relate to the room temperatures. Clever, eh?

The cabin-class lounge was situated on the promenade deck and was connected to the ball room, smoking room and bar. It had a stage, complete with all the necessary theatre accoutrements such as lighting and drop curtains. There was cinema screen at one end, and a large curved onyx fireplace at the other. Above the fireplace there is still a carved gesso panel depicting unicorns in battle, fashioned by Alfred J Oakley and Gilbert Bayes. Gesso is formed by mixing glue with plaster of Paris. It is then spread over a carved wood surface and then painted or gilded with gold leaf onto cream paint. The panel had some hinged doors which opened to reveal film projection equipment. The walls were covered with maple burr and it had a birch ceiling. The room was up lit by striking art deco alabaster torchieres, or urns. Each of the eight torchieres was carved from the same block of alabaster to ensure uniform colour and grain. The tables were made from maple burr to match the walls. The Wilton carpet could be rolled back to reveal the oak, mahogany and laurel wood parquet dance floor. Thirteen-foot-high windows lined the side aisle affording views of the ocean and promenade deck. Impressive by any standards.

These days, some of the décor might seem a little odd; the cabin-class bathrooms were panelled in Formica. At that time, Formica was new and ultra-fashionable. During the maiden voyage in May 1936, there had been no hand rails in the wood-panelled corridors. It had been thought that the ship would be too large and stable to need them. After a spell of extremely rough weather, it was decided that hand rails were needed, and to rectify the situation, plastic handrails were installed. Plastic was thought to be very modern at that time. The cabin-class bathrooms also had four water taps, for hot and cold fresh and salt water. Saltwater baths were much sought after, and some people thought they were more relaxing than freshwater baths. That said, there was only salt water available in the tourist and third-class accommodation. Our bathroom had four taps, but I was disappointed to find that there was no longer salt water on offer.

'A' deck was home to the cabin-class staterooms and suites. These were mostly panelled with light woods like bird's eye maple and Canadian birch. Apart from chairs and stools, the furniture was fully fitted and made from the same wood as the walls. Each of the fifty-four special state rooms on the main and A decks, was individually designed and decorated and had a telephone which was ultra-modern at that time. The Duke and Duchess of Windsor always booked the same suite of staterooms, M58 on the main deck. The chief steward made sure they were furnished with curtains and bedcovers in the Duchess' favourite colours of vibrant blues and greens.

Sadly, the increased desire and requirement for speed, and the growing popularity of air travel in the 1960s meant that the *Queen Mary* could not compete. Revenue plummeted and in 1967 she was purchased by the city of Long Beach in California; the plan was to use her as a tourist attraction and convention centre.

The ship was too large for the Panama Canal, and so her final voyage carried her 15,000 miles through Cape Horn and around South America. She was taken to a naval dry dock, the only one large enough in California, to be re-fitted before being taken to Long Beach, her final resting place.

During our stay on the *Queen Mary* we dined in Sir Winston's restaurant. It was our 20th wedding anniversary, and we toured the *Scorpion*, a Russian submarine that was docked alongside the ship. I felt very claustrophobic in the submarine. I take my hat off to submariners, I really don't know how they do it. The *Queen Mary* is well known to (allegedly) have paranormal hotspots and more than its fair share of ghosts. I would love to say I saw a ghost, or sensed a presence, but I didn't. Lisa, however, was rather troubled during our stay. She has always had psychic tendencies, just like my gran. Lisa could not sleep, and hence neither did Jemma. Lisa could hear voices, telephone conversations and thought there was a nasty storm going on outside when in fact it was very calm, but that is her story to tell. I can only say, that having witnessed many of Lisa's psychic experiences and feelings over the years, if she voices concern about something, which is thankfully rare, I sit up and take notice.

We ended our Californian tour back in San Francisco. The weather could have been better; there was a hazy fog over the water making it difficult to see the bright red Golden Gate Bridge. Mark Twain is believed to have said, *The coldest winter I ever spent was a summer in San Francisco.'* Whether he did or not, I really don't know, but we headed for the nearest shop that sold fleece jackets because we hadn't packed any.

The California sealions who hang out on the boat slips on pier 39's 'K' Dock were fascinating; we could have watched them all day as they hauled themselves up onto the slips, sunbathed and cried out 'arph arph arph' incessantly.

China town in San Francisco is the oldest in North America; it has the largest Chinese community outside Asia. It was quite a sight to behold, the colourful buzzing streets packed with Chinese speaking people. The shops displayed baskets and crates of unusual looking vegetables, fruits, herbs and teas, shoes and jewellery, all labelled in

Chinese. Disturbingly, especially for Jemma, who was a vegetarian at that time, there were live animal and fish markets. Wooden cages full of chickens, flapping about and clucking furiously, waiting to be chosen and eaten. I know I am a hypocrite when it comes to this; I enjoy meat and poultry, I just don't like knowing how they get onto my plate.

A boat trip to United States Penitentiary Alcatraz, now a national park, was a must. The day we chose to go was foggy, cold and wet, and the boat trip was very rough and choppy, but it seemed to add to the ambiance of the destination. Alcatraz was built as a federal government response to the problems which had arisen from the Depression and Prohibition. Famous inmates include George 'machine gun' Kelly, Robert 'the birdman of Alcatraz' Stroud, and of course all the way from Chicago, Al Capone. On the tour we learned that inmates had four rights, those being food, clothing, shelter and medical attention. Visits from family had to be earned, likewise with recreational pursuits such as reading or painting.

I was particularly interested in Al Capone. Firstly, because I enjoyed the film 'The Untouchables'. I do realise the claims it made about Elliot Ness, the prohibition agent famous for his attempts to bring down Al Capone, are somewhat exaggerated, and a good dash of poetic license was used, but I still enjoy watching it, and secondly, spending so much time in Chicago acting as a family tour guide, it was hard not to become clued-up about Alphonse and his infamous story.

Alphonse Capone was born in Brooklyn on the 18th of January 1899. His parents had immigrated to America from Italy. He moved to Chicago at the start of the prohibition era of 1920 to 1933 during which there was a nationwide constitutional ban on the production, importation or exportation of alcohol. Capone headed a crime empire by bootlegging (illegally making and selling alcohol) and gambling. He was dubbed 'Scarface' by the press because of deep scars sustained in 1917 during a fracas with a woman and her brother. He claimed he was doing the people of Chicago a favour and that he was providing a public service, saying that *'90% of the people of Cook County drank and gambled, and my offense has been to furnish them with those amusements'.*

Elliot Ness's team of officers were dubbed 'The Untouchables' because they were known not to take bribes. Although Ness did pursue Capone for his bootlegging and gambling, the government decided to concentrate on his tax evasion. Al Capone had agreed to a plea deal which would mean a maximum of two and a half years in prison. The judge, however, had other ideas, so Capone withdrew his guilty plea. The case went to trial, but the judge found out that some of the jurors had been bribed and switched the jury before the trial went ahead. Al Capone was sentenced to eleven years in prison and was fined $50,000. Some people wondered if transferring Mr. Capone to the newly opened and daunting facility of Alcatraz, a government publicity stunt, was to bring it to the attention of the American public. Who knows? Alcatraz operated as a US penitentiary for twenty-nine years.

In the 1960s, the island was occupied by native American Indians for eighteen months, firstly in 1964 and then again in 1969. The federal government planned to dissipate many of the Indian tribes, encouraging the Native Americans to move from reservations into cities using the 'Indian Termination Policy'. The occupation of the island had the desired effect and led to policy changes which meant many tribes that had inhabited America for thousands of years were saved.

CHAPTER 25

IT'S SO MUCH NICER TO COME HOME

– THE COTSWOLDS

"Think of England as a very large book. The Cotswolds would be an unfussy chapter in the middle somewhere where there is lots of limestone and even more sheep."

- Susan Meissner

In 2005, we returned to the UK. I was sad to leave the States, I had made friends and enjoyed the lifestyle, but I was also relieved to be going home, except, I didn't know where home was anymore. We had sold Warrender a couple of years before. I didn't ever see it empty, last time I saw it all our things were in there and somehow, my mind played tricks and told me it was still ours.

We were told that OH would be returning to work at British Energy's head office in Gloucester. The plan was that we would move into a hotel while we looked for a place to rent. This sounded like an adventure but was far from it. We ended up in the hotel for nine weeks and got to know every member of staff and knew every dish on the menu off by heart. I will never take making a slice of toast for supper or using a washing machine when I want to for granted ever again. Lisa was in an adjoining room for a while before she decided, quite wisely, to move up to Scotland which was where Jemma was at that time.

The very worst part of it all was that Bracken had been put in quarantine.

Before leaving for the States we had gone to the vet for advice. The Pet Passport had not yet been introduced, but the vet told us what was required. Bracken got his rabies and other vaccinations and he was microchipped. When we were living in America, Bracken had his annual rabies shots. What could possibly go wrong?

We decided that Jemma would fly home first and take Bracken with her. She was going to Scotland and so could leave him with Mum and Dad. He adored Dad and Dad adored him. Perfect solution to a potentially tricky situation. However, we received a tearful and angry phone call from Jemma. She was beside herself. Bracken had been put into kennels, and what is more, Jemma wasn't even allowed to see him, and the officials had been accusatory. We were all devastated, I don't even want to imagine what my poor boy was thinking about all this. He had been put in a UK Department for Environment, Food and Rural affairs recognised crate and flown home by Defra standards. He had all his vaccination records with him, we had no idea what had happened. It was so difficult being on the other side of the Atlantic; the time difference made it even more problematic. I don't think I slept for about a week. At first, we were told that he would be given an early release if we paid an extra £500, which we gladly did, but he was not released. It was explained to us that one of Bracken's rabies injections had been given two days late, two years previously. I couldn't understand what the problem was; if it was two years ago, and he had had blood tests done, which he did, how could he possibly be a risk to the UK rabies status? But it was decided that he was, and he spent the next six months in quarantine. To begin with he was in kennels at Heathrow. He was well looked after, but he couldn't see any other dogs from his pen and a 747 seemed to fly over every couple of minutes meaning that we could not hear ourselves think. We managed to get him moved to a kennel much closer to our hotel; he had a shelter, and an outside run where he could see the other dogs. The kennels were surrounded by trees and fields which he could see but not visit. Every day I would have breakfast and then pop over to the supermarket to buy some sandwiches and milk and then head to the kennel to visit my boy. I would borrow a towel from the hotel to sit on. There was a white plastic chair in his pen, but I preferred to sit on the ground beside him so that he could put his head on my lap and cuddle in. We would spend the day together, either outside in the run, under an umbrella if it was raining, or cooped up inside his sheltered area. He just lay beside me, resting his big soft black head on my knees and look at me with big brown super sad eyes. He wasn't allowed to wear his collar and he looked so abandoned. I truly thought my heart would break. The kennels played a radio through speakers around the grounds, and to this day, I can feel tears prick my eyes when I hear one of the songs that was played at that time.

We eventually found a house to rent in Bibury, a very beautiful and picturesque village in the Cotswolds. It had a large rather unkempt garden surrounded by a low dry-stone wall. There was a beautiful old stone stable in the garden. The house itself wasn't great, it had been built in the 1950s or 60s but it was in keeping with other houses in the area. Our garden had once belonged to the house next door, hence the stable and mature fruit trees. I thought the garden would be perfect for Bracken when we eventually got him home and I quite literally crossed the days off until the end of his incarceration on my kitchen calendar.

Directly behind the house was a church, in fact there was a gate leading from the garden into the church grounds. The house still belonged to the church and had been used by the church minister in the past. One of the first things I saw on moving in day was a coffin being carried into the small graveyard which was situated just to the left of the church. It was unexpected, but we had a very good view from the kitchen window!

Another incident which gave me a bit of a surprise was when I ventured into the stable for the first time. It was a beautiful little building. There was a staircase running up the left-hand, outside wall, leading to an entrance which had an old heavy wooden door. The main entrance at the front of the building did not have a door. The grass track leading to it was rather overgrown with nettles and brambles which I managed to cut back, allowing me access. I gingerly poked my head through the thick stone doorway and let out a shriek which brought Lisa running out. She had returned from Scotland and was preparing to move to Newcastle to study music. I couldn't believe my eyes. Standing in front of me were an almost life size Mary and Joseph, three wise men and inexplicably, a stuffed serpent lay on the ground. *What next?* I thought. Mrs. Bennet in Pride and Prejudice sprang to mind, I imagined her saying, 'You take delight in vexing me, have you no compassion for my poor nerves?'

It took over a week before our washing machine was delivered, and so I found myself handwashing clothes and hanging them out on the washing line which was suspended between three metal clothes poles, to drip dry. We were very close to the Royal Airforce base in Fairford and they were preparing for the annual air show. As I was hanging the shirts up, I planned to pick some fruit and then fetch some wood for the fire, which was the main source of heat in the house. We had storage heaters, but they weren't very effective. As I was standing there, WW2 aircraft droned past and the contrast between our house in America and the one we were in now hit me square between the eyes. There were no lampposts in the village, so at night, sitting just by the light of the coal fire, it was easy to imagine that I had somehow gone back in time.

Bibury was once described by William Morris (poet, novelist and textile designer 1834-1896) as *the most beautiful village in England*. And I can certainly agree with his sentiments.

The first time Jemma and Lisa saw it they thought it looked like 'The Shire' from the film 'Lord of the Rings' and exclaimed that it was a 'very Mum sort of place'. Bibury is named in the Domesday Book (1086) as 'Becheberie' so has been around for an extremely long time.

Arlington Row is very picturesque and charming. It was built in 1380 as a monastic wool store and was converted into weavers' cottages in the 17th century. Whenever I was walking there I would see Japanese tourists, often with easels, painting the row. Apparently, it became a popular Japanese tourist destination after Emperor Hirohito spent some time in Bibury during his European tour in the first half of the 20th century; he was a big fan and who can blame him? The cloth produced in the weavers' cottages was sent to the nearby Arlington Mill.

Jemma returned home for a short while and worked in the Bibury Court Hotel. It is a beautiful Jacobean building, built in 1633. She worked as a waitress and served in the bar for a while. I believe it has closed now which is a great shame. It was more like visiting old friends than a hotel; boots came off at the door, there was always a roaring log fire and old, squidgy chintz sofas. Dogs were more than welcome which was a boon when Bracken was eventually released from captivity. When Jemma's shift was due to end, I would walk down to the hotel with Bracken to meet her, usually about eleven at night. Bracken had a habit of sitting on chairs just like a human, rear end on the seat, front paws on the floor. Being in the Bibury Court did not stop him, much to the amusement of the staff and my embarrassment. Jemma would often have a doggy bag of cooked pheasant or some other gastronomic leftovers for Bracken as a present from the chef and we would walk back along the River Coln, occasionally shining our torches onto the water to look at the numerous slumbering ducks. They would sometimes quack with annoyance, albeit rather halfheartedly, at this nocturnal intrusion.

Bracken was released on the 4th of December 2005, one day after my birthday. I was up at the crack of dawn, anxious not to waste one precious minute of his liberation. When we walked in with his collar and lead, the normally gentle and docile boy nearly knocked me over. He knew he was being released from his doggy prison cell. Ecstatically, he made for some trees, sniffed the air and the grass, and generally looked very happy and pleased with himself. It was a joy to watch him taking in his surroundings and nature for the first time in six months. I took him for a short walk around the village when we got home and then we lay end to end on the sofa and slept a deep, blissful and contented sleep. Things were back just as they should be, my boy was home.

I had noticed a little cat sitting in the garden, usually by the rather stagnant, and smelly pond under some trees. Lisa had wanted a cat ever since she was little and so was particularly interested in this little bundle of black and white fur. We discovered she was allergic to cats when we stayed with friends who had two of them, giving us the perfect excuse not to consider having one of our own. I had never been a big cat fan if truth be told, so I wasn't overly upset about her allergy.

One day, when Lisa was at home, we saw that the little cat had crept into the kitchen and was eating some of Bracken's food. Bracken merely looked from the cat to us with an incredulous sort of expression on his face. That night there was a dreadful storm and I noticed that the poor little thing was under the car trying to shelter from the pelting rain. It was a pitiful sight. I opened the front door and she shot in, shaking her fur and making indigent mewing noises, as if to say, 'Well you took your time.' From that day on I started to buy cat food as well as dog food when I went to Cirencester for the weekly groceries. We made posters with her photograph on them and I asked neighbours if they knew who she could belong to, but to no avail. We now had a cat, and I must admit, I was secretly delighted. OH reminded us that terms of our let stated only one pet allowed. So anytime she was in the house when he arrived home from work, we opened the window and popped her into the garden. She really was the sweetest little cat; she had a small round face and a determined little nose. She seemed to be independent, and yet there was a vulnerability about her and she adored being stroked and fussed over. Her little white bib was kept spotless by her sandpaper-like tongue, she had white paws which made her look like she was wearing little white socks on the end of her furry black legs.

I had started working full time in the Winfield Hospital in Gloucester. As luck would have it, my boss, Gaynor, was a real cat lover, and delightedly brought in a spare cat carry box she had, plus some cat dishes and a litter tray. It was official. We were cat owners. We took her to the vet; she wasn't microchipped, and the vet said he thought she was about six years old. I watched in amazement and delight the first time I saw her use the litter tray; she knew exactly what to do and was very precise. She had obviously once belonged to someone, but who? And how had she ended up coming to a house with a big black dog in it? We never did find out. Lisa made posters and put them up around Arlington and Bibury, and I asked at the post office if anyone had lost a cat but nothing or rather no one was forthcoming. Polly became one of the family and we loved her.

Figure 45: *Bracken in Bibury*

I had been looking for a job for quite some time before my interview at the Winfield. I was looking for another practice nurse post, but the fact that I had been in America and not gainfully employed for some time seemed to put perspective employers off quite a bit, I saw the advert for an outpatient nurse in, yes, you've guessed it, the local paper. I reckoned I had the necessary skills, and decided to apply, but I had no idea at that time what type of establishment the Winfield actually was.

I was very pleasantly surprised, it was a large private hospital, very well structured with a soothing elegant décor in the reception where I was asked to wait. I was interviewed by the Matron and by my boss-to-be, Gaynor, a lovely soft-spoken Welsh lady. I answered the questions to the best of my ability and thought it had gone quite well when Matron said that the successful candidate would be notified by telephone that evening before the letters went out to the others. I jokingly said that if it was me, not to call between seven thirty and eight because I was a Coronation Street fan and there was an exciting story line going on. I left thinking what an idiot I had been, blown it at the last hurdle, but by the time I got home there was a message on the answering machine offering me the position and telling me to enjoy Corrie!

Wendy Hatchet, one of the outpatient receptionists I got on particularly well with, and who does not suffer fools gladly, has never let me forget that I was off sick before I even got started. I had been anxious to get our wild garden under some sort of control before I started work and had been working flat out digging, weeding, trimming trees and bushes, and the inevitable happened. Dependable as ever, my back, undoubtedly reacting to the stress of my forthcoming new post and the manual labour went into a major spasm. I lost all the feeling in my right leg and was constantly falling over. When I did start work my short-sleeved, pin-striped and epauletted uniform did nothing to hide the mass of bruises I had sustained on the stairs if I forgot to lead with my left foot and not my right.

Wendy, a tall glamourous lady who was always immaculately made up and had long painted fingernails, was a big fan of Scotsmen, and the bagpipes. She loved to call me 'hen' (she still does). Apparently, she started to learn how to play the bagpipes but couldn't blow and play a tune with her fingers at the same time, so her husband Ges used to do the blowing for her. I cannot erase that visualisation from my mind!

I used to listen to Radio 2 when driving to work and was often amused by Sir Terry Wogan and his made-up names. One quiet clinic day, I decided to play a trick on Wendy. The clinic lists were typed up by the medical secretaries in advance of the clinics, but often patients were added at the last minute which meant searching for case notes which could be easier said than done at times. I told her that a military man had been added to a clinic and that he insisted upon being called Major, I added him to the list as Major Eisewater. I also said there was a young lad coming in called Justin and added Justin Payne to the clinic list. Unfortunately, I was called away to help with a minor operation in the treatment room and could not oversee these new clinic additions. Apparently, there was chaos as medical secretaries claimed to know nothing about these additions or where the notes were.

Wendy also created and produced a hospital magazine on a quarterly basis called *Winfield Whispers* in which she included competitions, jokes, stories of interest and a 'Guess who did this' section. I seemed to feature in every issue. It went a bit like this:

'Who couldn't remember which switch was up and which was down on her soft top car when the mechanism jammed and entertained other motorists while her top went up and down incessantly in a traffic jam?'

'Who ended up with Dr Adrianne's lipstick imprint on her right boob and left powdery (from surgical gloves) handprints on Dr Adrienne's shoulders after a collision in the corridor?'

'Who managed to scald her left armpit with a red-hot damp tea towel whilst hemming her uniform using wundaweb?'

I met so many wonderful people at the Winfield. I will be forever indebted to many of them for their kindness, support and friendship in the following years. You know who you are, Lucy, Ali, Maria, Ruth, Wendy, Irene and especially Rita and Vic.

One of the first things Gaynor said to me after I started working at the Winfield was, 'I hope you aren't too ambitious, because I am afraid around here promotion is a case of filling dead men's shoes.' These words still haunt me.

Not too long after I had been there, Gaynor promoted me to senior staff nurse. I was to act as deputy in her absence, when she was on holiday or off sick. I was delighted to say the least, it proved I had not let her down when she took a gamble on someone who had not practiced for several years. Gaynor was the type of person who would not only buy the big issue, she would buy presents for the vendor, especially at Christmas, her favourite time of year. She made me a Christmas pudding one year, but wouldn't allow me to have the recipe; it was a traditional Welsh recipe, a family secret and absolutely delicious.

This reminds me of a winter tale she once told me. Gaynor had been looking after an old gentleman who was suffering greatly from pressure sores. The ward was a large nightingale type but had verandas around it which in years gone by were used in the summer for patients who were suffering from tuberculosis. Sunshine was thought to be therapeutic for these patients.

The ward Sister had instructed that the gentleman should have an air ring. Nurses always had these to hand on the wards. They were usually made of a circle of thick foam, hollow in the middle like a donut. They were placed in a pillow case and put under a patient to take pressure off the sacral area when they were sitting for any length of time.

It was later in the day when Sister noticed that the patient had been gone from his bedside for quite some time.

'Where is Mr. Smith?' asked Sister curiously.

'He is still outside,' replied Gaynor, feeling pleased with herself.

'What on earth is he doing outside? He will freeze to death in this weather,' cried Sister in alarm.

'But Sister, you told me to give him an airing,' said Gaynor, shocked and surprised by Sister's reaction.

Seemingly the old chap was none the worse for his hefty dose of fresh air, and absolutely fine after being wrapped in a warm blanket and being given a strong cup of tea.

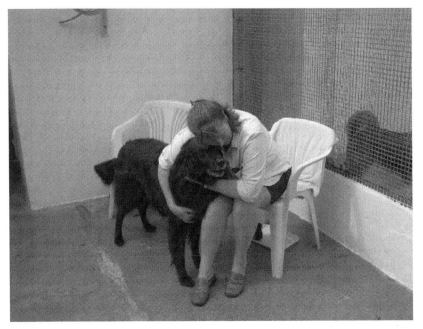

Figure 46: *Bracken in quarantine*

Figure 47: *Polly puss cat*

I was with Gaynor the day she found out she had pancreatic cancer. She had taken an unusually long lunch break. She hadn't been feeling too well for quite some time and had made an appointment to see one of our consultants. That day, she had gone around to radiology to ask if her test results had come back yet. The radiology manager was a very good friend of hers and apparently, she could not meet Gaynor's steady gaze as she asked about the results. Gaynor later told me that she knew immediately that something was terribly wrong. When she walked into the duty room I too could tell that something bad had happened. It was dreadful. I immediately called Matron who came around and handled the situation in her usual calm and clearheaded manner.

I cannot begin to imagine what Gaynor and her family went through at that time. Gaynor remained very upbeat and positive and was calm and dignified to the very end. It was a heartbreakingly sad time.

Naturally, Gaynor was off sick for a long time and I found myself in charge of the department. Another baptism of fire, but the experience proved to be invaluable and essential for my future.

My beloved boy Bracken seemed to be breathless at times and was slowing down quite a bit. A visit to the vet for an ECG and cardiac echo scan confirmed that he had a heart condition called cardiomyopathy and would require long-term medication. He seemed to be responding quite well to his treatment and short gentle walks, but it was obvious that his condition was getting worse. We travelled to Scotland just after Christmas in 2006 and he became much worse. He was staying with Mum and Dad, my mother- and father-in-law had a German Shepherd, and the two dogs did not get along too well. I decided to stay at Mum and Dad's too, to be with him. I called our vet in Cirencester for advice. I sat up with him all night, calling the vet several more times; he advised me to take him to a local vet in the morning. Bracken looked worn out and as I gazed into his eyes, they seemed distant and resigned. It was one of the longest nights of my life. OH returned in the morning and we took him to the vet Dad had used for Rex.

The vet, very matter-of-factly said there was nothing he could do and that the only kind thing to do was to put Bracken to sleep. It all happened very quickly, and Bracken was manoeuvred, rather roughly I thought, into the middle of the floor as the vet filled his syringe. I knelt beside him and did not stop gazing into his eyes as I stroked him and spoke softly to him as he drifted off into oblivion. I was inconsolable and will never ever forget my boy who had been by my side through thick and thin. Who loved me unconditionally. There will always be a special part in my heart just for him and I think of him every day.

The first time I got home from work after Bracken died was dreadful. He was usually at the top of the stairs looking out of the window in the stairwell and would bark with delight when he saw me. I opened the door with tears in my eyes and there was Polly, sitting right by the door. She had never done that before and it was such a comfort. She allowed me to pick her up and cuddle her and didn't even seem to mind her little head getting wet with tears.

Another devastating blow was about to strike out at us. My mother-in law became ill almost overnight. She was the type of person who was always busy. She cooked, baked, sewed, made marmalade and jam, could knit amazing jumpers and cardigans, rarely watched television and was a real go-to person in times of crisis. A brain tumour was diagnosed. She fought against this merciless monster within her, but after several short months, it won the battle and she died aged just sixty years old. Her mother had lived to a ripe old age, and Joan was quite a bit younger than my father-in-law, so again, the unexpectedness and unfairness seemed almost too difficult to comprehend. She was a lovely lady, and I am thankful that I got to know her so much better when we were living in America when I spent so much time with her. We developed an understanding between us and the bond between us grew. It was a devastatingly tragic way for such a vibrant lifeforce to end, and I still miss her and think of her often.

*

It should have been very clear to me that my marriage was coming to an end; maybe it was all the sad events which had happened in recent months, I will never know, but that deceitful brain of mine was at it again and was choosing not to acknowledge what was blatantly obvious. I had experienced a certain amount of déjà vu in recent months, reminding me of my first few months in America. We were both miserable and seemed to resent each other in many ways, but in the end, it was he who called it a day after accusations and arguments.

A lawyer in Cheltenham was recommended by one of the consultants at the Winfield. I made an appointment and my friend and colleague, Lucy, accompanied me for support and to remind me of what was said. It seemed surreal at the time, and I wasn't sure what to expect, but the solicitor simply said, 'We need to get you out of this situation,' and there it was, a reality check, and I knew there would be no going back. As ever, the timing couldn't have been worse, I was going through peri-menopause. I was gaining weight, having hot flushes, menorrhagia and night sweats. My hormones were all over the place and I often felt quite ill and worn out. I am sure any woman who has experienced it will empathise, but it is not only the physical changes which have an impact. There are huge emotional connotations. I felt mournful about a phase of my life which was coming to an end, I felt useless and old, so the impact, when I found out that OH was having a relationship with a girl who was more than twenty years younger than I was, could not have hit me harder. He flew off to meet her leaving me feeling very alone and very scared, but I used the week he was away to get my thoughts together and plan for my future. At that time, the Winfield was my saving grace. It was the place where I could relax and talk with friends; home was now a strange hostile environment and I did not want to spend any more time there than I had to. Friends rallied round and offered me a bed for the night when I needed it. It was amazing, these people who were great work colleagues became good friends. None more so than Rita and Vic, husband and wife who worked at the hospital. They were about the same age as my mum and dad and they opened their home and their hearts to me. Rita kept 'my' bed made up and told me I could stay as often and for as long as I needed to. They offered sound advice, told it like it was, and tried to convince me that once the divorce was over, I would move forward and not look back. I truly do not know what I would have done without them; they are genuine, wise and amazing people. I could not have got through it without Wendy's wit and wisdom, common sense and packing skills, Alison for accompanying me when I went flat hunting and then helping me to move in to it, Maria for her friendship, kindness, humour and practicality Lucy, for being a good friend and coming with me to the solicitors and just knowing the right thing to say at the right time. Ruth for being like a mother hen and always keeping her door open for me, and Irene for her support both practical and psychological. What they did for me is living proof of the true spirit of human kindness. They told me that I would always have a bed in their homes and they genuinely meant it. Priceless.

I spent most weekends working in the garden and watching television. I was living in what had been our room. I made sure to have my main meal at work and made do with a microwave meal at night and usually a bottle of wine, living the dream.

I often went for a walk around Bibury and Arlington. I loved to go to the Church of St Mary and enjoy the total peace, serenity and tranquillity it had to offer. I listened to the soothing choral music, and chatted to Gran, silently of course. I always felt better when I had been in there, refreshed almost, and ready to take on the next challenge.

I was not looking for another job; leaving the Winfield at that time, my one familiar and comfortable place, seemed unthinkable, but, while I was checking my work emails, a job vacancy flashed up on the screen. It was an internal advertisement for an outpatient manager at Pinehill Hospital in Hitchin, Hertfordshire. I had no idea where Hitchin was, and was about to close the screen when Lorraine, one of my colleagues who had been looking over my shoulder as I read out the details said, 'That's your job,' very matter-of-factly. Just a year ago, applying would not have crossed my mind, but since Gaynor's illness and tragic death, I had gained management experience and, just as importantly, confidence. Now that I had accepted the inevitability of a divorce, I felt free and more lighthearted than I had in years. I applied.

I had also decided that sauce for the goose was indeed sauce for the gander and joined the Friends Reunited dating site. This was to be a life-changing decision and I would meet the love of my life… but not yet. I got an immediate reply from what I thought seemed like a nice man with a friendly face. He was keen to meet up, but I had commitments including a trip to Scotland and had to put him off for a while. I enjoyed the emails and calls that had started between us. He called me while I was on the train to Scotland and wished me a safe journey, and we arranged a date to meet.

Our first encounter was at the Bibury Court Hotel where I was wined and dined in style by Mr. B. We had a lovely evening and I certainly had a spring in my step when I told the girls at work about it the next day. I explained what he did for a living and told them his name. Maria looked pensive for a moment and then Googled him. *Uh oh*, I thought, *knew it was too good to be true*. She asked me to look at the screen, and there he was, my date from last night and it turned out that he was a multi-millionaire. I hadn't felt married for a long time and so did not feel guilty about seeing someone else after what seemed to be such a short time after separating. I occasionally arranged to meet Mr. B at his house (well, one of them) and his boat, and was wined and dined in style. It was fun, and it certainly did my self-esteem a world of good, but there was something missing. For a start, I did not know how much he could be trusted, which was the most important thing for me, and I suspected he wasn't in it for the long haul, but then neither was I. I enjoyed his company and he seemed to enjoy mine which was all that mattered at that time.

It was around this time that I met Jilly Cooper. She lived nearby and could often be seen in the area. I told her that she was my dog

Jilly's namesake and she couldn't have been more delighted and gave me a huge hug, truly delighted. I admit I felt a bit nervous about telling her; not everyone would be pleased about having a dog named after them. She was vexed when I told her about Bracken having been in quarantine and the circumstances which led to it.

'I wish I had known you then,' she exclaimed. 'We could have had a double page spread in the *Daily Mail*.'

What a genuinely lovely lady. She gave me her phone number in case I was interested in adopting a greyhound; she had just adopted one which she called Feather and she told me that he was delightful, but unfortunately it was not the right time or place for me.

*

I was invited for an interview at Pinehill. It was owned by the same company as the Winfield, and so seemed very familiar and I instantly felt at home. Once again, my back was playing up big time. I had just spent a week in Scotland visiting my parents, played golf with Dad and failed to travel light as usual. While I was moving my suitcase at Birmingham New Street, I felt a familiar twang in my lower back, but fear of missing my connection and adrenaline kept me moving. So here I was, having what potentially was a life-changing interview and I was limping and finding it difficult to move. The physiotherapist at Winfield had suggested that I should use a walking stick, but I was determined that I would get through my interview stickless.

I met Jemma in London after the interview. I was delighted when I discovered that if I got the job, I would be about a half-hour train journey from where she was living at that time.

I received the phone call telling me I had been successful while I was at work. I was so shocked I had to sit down. This was it, a fresh new beginning. The next few weeks and months were manic as I looked for somewhere to live and sourced a man with a van to help me move. It felt exhilarating and petrifying. While I was sitting at lunch one day, I happened to mention that I was going to Hitchin to look at flats and Alison Herbert, one of the theatre sisters, offered to come with me. I was so grateful to her and would probably have taken the first place on offer if she hadn't been there to guide me. Alison is a giver, she works on Mercy Ships and travels the world, working hands on in aid of charity.

That Saturday it was beautiful and sunny. Hitchin is an attractive market town and as Alison and I sat outside on the grass munching sandwiches we had bought from a delicatessen, I had an overwhelming feeling that everything was going to be just fine.

I had several leaving do's and was presented with beautiful flowers, a fob watch, and lovely red Parker pen and a satnav. My sense of direction was somewhat notorious and the people at work thought they might never see me again if I didn't own one. I am certain I have Alison to thank for suggesting that as a gift.

*

Wendy came around and helped me pack my things, carefully wrapping dishes and ornaments in newspaper, and Alison helped me on moving out day; it was another Saturday. I had been staying with her for a few days before I moved and so we drove to my old home together. As soon as we arrived OH left, and I must say I was thankful for that. It soon became obvious that everything I had hoped to take would not fit in the small white van I had hired, Alison, without prompting or giving it a second thought, offered to drive down with me and started to load up her four-by-four after calling her husband to tell him she would be later than planned. She was truly selfless and amazing. I cried when I said goodbye to little Polly. She looked at me as if to say, 'It's okay, I understand I am not allowed in your new house.' I hated leaving her behind, but there was nothing else I could do.

It was pouring with rain by the time we reached Letchworth, which was where I had I rented a small one-bedroom house. Lisa was travelling by train to help me move in too. Alison went to fetch her from the station, having never met her before, but found her through a process of elimination. By the time all the boxes were in the living room we were exhausted and dripping wet with rain. Alison had thoughtfully packed some homemade cake and other goodies, so we had a quick cup of tea before Alison set off for home. Lisa and I then headed for the nearest supermarket to buy something for dinner and I panicked slightly when I couldn't remember how to get back to the house without the satnav, which had been left in the house.

It didn't take too long to get unpacked, and quite soon, it looked quite comfortable and welcoming. My next big challenge was starting my new job on Wednesday.

*

Pinehill is a lovely hospital in Hitchin. It is set in beautiful grounds and is surrounded by trees and greenery. It is relatively small as hospitals go, and that meant that very soon I knew everyone who worked there. The outpatients nurses were as inquisitive about me as I was about them and turned out to be a great team who worked well together. I was made to feel very welcome and soon settled into a routine.

I arrived in what was Pinehill's centenary year; it had been built in 1908 by Frank Newton and was used as a convalescent hospital, taking in patients from a German hospital in London. Patients were sent to Hitchin to rest and recuperate in the clean, fresh, Hertfordshire air. It was run by a team of nurses who came from an epileptic institution in the town of Bethel, situated on the Rhine in Germany. After the outbreak of war in 1914, the war office took it over and used it to care for British soldiers. It really is a beautiful old building and it oozes character and charm. The centenary ball was held the month after I started work there and was held in a marquee in the grounds. I had thought about inviting Mr. B; he had already paid me a visit and taken me to dinner at Red Coats, but I decided that I should concentrate on my career and that men would need to take a back seat for a long time. Lisa accompanied me, and we literally had a ball! It was a wonderful way to meet everyone socially and I really felt like I belonged there.

It was a challenging time, but I thrived on it. I found that I was really enjoying my new life, Rita and Vic had been right after all.

Not long after the ball I received a message through the Friends Reunited site from a man who sounded friendly and funny. He had moved to Letchworth the same August weekend as I had, in similar circumstances, and said he missed going out for a good curry. Reading between the lines, I guessed he was a policeman. He really seemed to like motorbikes, which I found slightly off putting, because I have never been a fan of them since working on ward six, but, after asking Lisa to take a look at his profile, I decided to meet him for a curry in one of the local Indian restaurants. I drove there so that I could make a quick getaway if need be. I parked my old Saab convertible and walked up Station Road towards the restaurant. There was no one standing outside, but I noticed a man across the street looking in a shop window. Instinctively I called out, 'Mike,' and he turned around and headed towards me. We exchanged pleasantries and went inside. He was driving too, so the restaurant did a roaring trade in Diet Coke and tap water that night. We talked about our work, our families and reminisced about hospital Casualty departments on Saturday nights. Mike had been with the Metropolitan Police Force, in the traffic department, hence his affinity with motorbikes. I explained that almost every young man in my first ward had come off or been knocked off a motorbike and then the stories just started pouring out of us. We laughed and chatted all night until one of the waiters informed us that they were waiting to close.

We had both parked in the same car park, so we walked sedately down Station Road towards our cars, about a foot apart. We agreed that we would like to see each other again. We both thought, *The sooner the better,* but neither said it out loud. Mike was overseeing major renovations to the bungalow he had just bought but said some time off for a coffee the next day would be welcome. He came around at the time he said he would and apologised for not bringing flowers. It was a Sunday and the only flowers he could find were in the garage forecourt and he thought they looked tacky. I loved his honesty, lack of pretence, his wit and his genuine warmth, all of which had been missing from my life for a very long time. I instinctively knew that this big gentle man would be trustworthy and do me no harm. Mr. B was history from that moment on. Qualities like Mike's are priceless. He is the love of my life, and I really do not know what I have done to deserve the adoration of such a loving man who truly believes in me.

We saw each other every day after our first meeting and continued to laugh every day. Mike was a big hit with Lisa, and Jemma. The first Christmas the four of us spent together was peaceful and magical.

*

I was chatting to one of the girls at work one day, and she happened to mention her friend's mother, Iris, was a psychic medium. She told me that she did not believe in such things and would never have sought any information. She explained that she had experienced a miscarriage in the past and when she became pregnant again absolutely no one knew about it. She wanted to wait until she was at the three of four months stage before telling anyone. She bumped into her friend's mum purely by chance at a village fete. Iris had put her hand on her shoulder and told her not to worry, everything would be just fine this time. My ears immediately pricked up. I felt it was time to fulfil the promise I made to Gran all those years ago, and I asked for Iris's number.

I called Iris, and a very friendly homely voice said she would be delighted to see me, and I made an appointment. The night I drove there, I was very nervous, my palms felt clammy and I had copious butterflies swarming around in my stomach. I needn't have worried. Iris answered the door and invited me in. It was a bit like visiting a favourite auntie, I immediately felt relaxed and at home. She made a big mug of tea and we started to chat. I had made up my mind only to answer questions with a yes or no, and to give nothing away.

When I left, after about three hours, I truly felt that I had spent a wonderful evening with my grandparents. A few things had puzzled me, but when I got home and listened to the tape recording, one by one they fell into place. She had mentioned something to do with a maths teacher and blue bells, she kept saying bell, it meant nothing to me. She also said that Gran had not liked my first boyfriend, that he was not good enough for me. Again, I couldn't understand. My first boyfriend had been when I was fourteen years old, and he hadn't met anyone in my family. When I listened to the tape I understood with a start, that the boyfriend she had been talking about, was Mr. B, and the teacher was Miss Bell who lived across the street from Mum and Dad. She had taught Dad at school, and occasionally I would go over to her with my sums (never my strong point) to ask for help.

Iris also told me that I was separated from my husband and that it was a good thing. She said both of my girls had psychic tendencies, but one more than the other, and she saw confetti. She told me I would get married again and that I had already met the man who would become my husband (Mike and I were certain that neither of us was interested in getting married again).

She talked about when I was a baby, bathed in front of a coal fire and splashing so much that raincoats and newspapers had to be spread around the baby bath. I knew about this, I had been told about it often enough when I was growing up and used to get extremely embarrassed by it. She told me that Papa had been mixed up before he died, that he knew he was ill and confused, she also told me that I had been the apple of his eye because I was the first grandchild, and I had been told that before too.

Iris did not mention Scotland, I thought she would because of my accent, but she did mention America and the Cotswolds. She spoke about a mill, and again I didn't know what she meant, and then I remembered that there was a huge water mill in Arlington just down from where we lived; it had been an antique shop at that time, and I hadn't thought of it as a mill. She also told me that Gran could hear me talking to her when I sat in the church, and that she had tried to send me messages and leave signs that she was with me, but that I never noticed them. Iris told me that Gran was so pleased that I had reached my full potential at work too. I also believe that Joan who had been my mother-in-law and her mother Gran Storrar sent me a message too, and Beth Masterton who had been my neighbour in North Berwick. All of this was so unexpected. I called Dad when I got home and described a man who smoked a pipe to him. Iris had told me this man was there with me. Dad got a bit choked up and said I had just described his granta. I was overwhelmed and truly wished I had gone to visit a medium sooner, but I do believe there is a time and place for everything, and that my timing was just right.

Life continued happily and contentedly as normal. Mike and I did get married on the 23rd of April 2012. Yes, I married my Englishman on St George's day, a very intimate affair held in Hatfield Registry Office with Jemma and her fiancé Andy, Lisa and her husband Alex, and Mike's Dad in attendance. The ceremony was followed by a meal in Letchworth Hall Hotel which is a beautiful building; it was built in 1625, and had stunning fireplaces and oak panelling which made it the perfect setting for a celebratory meal.

I was extremely happy at Pinehill, and in time several colleagues became good friends. They had arranged an amazing hen night for me. Madeleine Smith was the instigator and chief organiser. She took us to a place where we were encouraged to dance on the tables after we had eaten. It was the chief selling point! Madeleine drove the mini bus to and from the venue too, what a star, especially on the return journey with a van load of tipsy nurses who had trouble remembering where they lived. Lesley and I shared the same taste in classical music and often went on trips to the Royal Albert Hall to be astounded by the Classical Spectacular with its rousing finale of cannons and fireworks as the orchestra played Tchaikovsky's 1812 Overture.

One Christmas, Elaine, Lesley and I went to the RAH for a Christmas sing-along concert. We were singing along at the top of our voices, when I got my words mixed up (not unusual for me. I have to say, in the past I have called lettuce 'tricel', macaroni cheese 'cheese de macacha', and elderflower water 'elderwoerfloter' to name but a few) and instead of singing 'corn for popping', I loudly sang 'porn for cocking'. Oh, the humiliation.

On the 29th of April 2011, I found myself in London with Jemma and Lisa to celebrate the wedding of Prince William and Kate Middleton.

At that time Jemma was working in the QEII Conference Centre, the largest conference, events and exhibition venue in London. It is in the heart of Westminster and has excellent views of Westminster Abbey where the couple were to be married.

Jemma was given the opportunity to attend the breakfast and lunch parties being held there and to invite a couple of guests, enter Lisa and me.

On the morning of the 29th, we got suitably dressed up and set off for Westminster. As we walked through the city streets, which were already crowded, we could hear music which seemed to be coming from speakers in the street. When Handel's Zadok the Priest was played I got goosebumps. The atmosphere in the QEII venue was electric with anticipation. As well as being able to view the Abbey plus the television crews and cameras from all over the world, the room we were in had massive screens broadcasting the wedding live. We watched the guests arrive and eventually, the Royal Family started to appear. It was so exciting to watch the bride emerge from her car in her stunning dress. After the ceremony was over we enjoyed an opulent lunch before going outside to join the thousands of people who were thronging through the streets. It was like attending a massive party, the joyfulness was palpable. We watched the yellow RAF rescue helicopter fly overhead; it was a truly memorable day.

*

We were soon reunited with Polly. OH was moving to a new

house too, and couldn't take her with him, and it was with sheer joy and delight that we welcomed her back into the fold. That said, the first night I left Mike alone with her was a bit of a disaster. I had gone to Covent Garden with Jemma and Lisa to meet friends who were over from America. We had a lovely evening, but I knew that I would have to be very quiet when I got home because Mike was on early shift the next morning and would have gone to bed early. When I arrived at the bungalow expecting peace and quiet, all the lights were on which was most unusual. I entered the hall and my olfactory nerve was sickened by the smell which was permeating through the house. When I went into the kitchen I saw blood on the walls. I was horrified. What on earth had happened?

He later told me that he had been awoken by Polly's piercing, agitated and relentless meowing. He got up to investigate and noticed that she was hiding behind the boiler in the kitchen which was still in the middle of being renovated. Then, out of the corner of his eye, he saw Polly sitting in the dining room. He went back to the boiler cupboard, and sure enough there was a black and white cat in there too. Which one was Polly? After further investigation, he established that the cat in the dining room was Polly, and so he set about getting the other cat out into the garden. This was easier said than done, and the cat began to screech and tear around the kitchen wall for all it was worth before disappearing out the back door. Obviously, there had been some altercation between the two cats and Polly had won. Polly was a very small cat and quite timorous. The mayhem that evening took its toll. Just as Mike had snuggled back into bed, he became aware of a strange gurgling noise beside him as Polly discharged the contents of her bowel and it went gushing all over the duvet. As I pieced together the events which had taken place, I recalled asking Mike, not that many weeks ago, if he minded having a cat, and saying, 'Honestly, she will be no trouble at all.'

*

One day, I got a phone call while I was on an early shift at Pinehill. It was Mike telling me that he had just spoken to a chap from a nursing agency who told him that he had a job I might be interested in. I wasn't looking for another job. Pinehill was a ten-minute (on a good day) drive from home, I knew everyone, and was quite settled, but I was intrigued. I vaguely remembered registering with the agency a long time ago but had completely forgotten all about it. I called the chap back, and before I knew where I was I had arranged a visit to The Lister Hospital in Chelsea.

Figure 48: *Alastair, Jacqueline and Jim*

Figure 49: *Jacqueline's 50th birthday at Pinehill*

CHAPTER 26

THE LISTER HOSPITAL

"If the love of surgery is a proof of a person's being adapted for it, then certainly I am fitted to be a surgeon; for thou can'st hardly conceive what a high degree of enjoyment I am from day to day experiencing in this bloody and butchering department of the healing art. I am more and more delighted with my profession."

- Joseph Lister

The Lister Hospital is in the west end of London on the Chelsea Embankment, and is currently owned by the Hospital Corporation of America. The hospital as we know it today, opened its doors in 1985. The original part of the building was once the premises of the Institute of Preventative Medicine, designed by architect Alfred Waterhouse and built on land provided by the Duke of Westminster in 1891. The Institute, which also had premises in Sudbury and Elstree, researched the cause, prevention and treatment of disease becoming renowned in microbiology, bacteriology, virology and protozoology (study of protozoa which are single-celled organisms for example, some fungi, algae and slime moulds). The Institute prepared and supplied vaccines and antitoxins to prevent diseases such as smallpox, typhoid, diphtheria and tetanus. They also pioneered the preparation of dried human plasma for transfusion.

In 1898 It was renamed the Jenner Institute after Edward Jenner who had created the smallpox vaccine and again in 1903 as The Lister Institute in honour of Joseph Lister and his revolutionary work in surgery and aseptic techniques. Until 1914 it was the only organisation of its kind in the country and was ranked throughout the world with the Rockefeller Institute in New York and the Pasteur Institute in Paris.

Joseph Lister who later became Lord Lister, was born in Essex in 1827. By all accounts the young man excelled at languages but was attracted and drawn towards medicine. He graduated with honours from the University of London in 1852, and that same year, he was elected as a Fellow of the Royal College of Surgeons.

Joseph moved to the city of Edinburgh in 1853 to study with the renowned and ground-breaking surgeon Professor James Syme. Lister intended to study and work with the professor for a month. He became Syme's first assistant (his right-hand man during surgical operations) and eventually married Professor Syme's daughter Agnes. He lived in Edinburgh much longer than one month, twenty-four years to be exact.

Joseph Lister had been inspired by Louis Pasteur, the French chemist who proved that infection was caused by organisms so small that they were invisible to the naked eye. Pasteur knew that these organisms could be removed by filtration, by heat or by chemicals. Since the first two methods were not possible with human patients, Joseph concentrated on the latter. He learned that carbolic acid might kill bacteria and so he began to use it as an antiseptic when he operated on his patients. It did kill bacteria and it consequently, saved lives. Lister went on to operate on Queen Victoria and was knighted in 1882. He was called to assist with surgery performed on King Edward VII in 1902. The king had been suffering from recurrent abdominal pain, rigors and a mass was found in the lower right quadrant of his abdomen; all are symptoms of appendicitis. In the end, his appendix was not removed, but after the administration of ether anaesthetic, the abscess was drained, irrigated and packed with gauze and rigid rubber tubing was left in situ to allow further drainage of pus. Patients often died with complications of appendicitis in those days, perforations, peritonitis and sepsis being the main culprits. The King thankfully survived, and his now postponed coronation went ahead in August of that year.

*

My first visit to The Lister was on a rather grey frosty day, but that did not mar my experience. I love London, almost as much as Mike now detests it having worked there for so many years. Any time I had visited the capital city I got a buzz, a feeling of exhilaration, and excitement just being there. But this was different, and I knew it. What would it be like to work there, to have a daily commute by train to King's Cross, then on the tube to Victoria Station and then either a walk or the number 44 bus to Chelsea Bridge Road SW1W no less?

As I walked along Chelsea Bridge Road, I could see Battersea Power station ahead of me. The home of the Chelsea Flower Show was across the street. Behind me was the Royal Hospital Chelsea, home of the Chelsea pensioners. I could see Chelsea Bridge with the Thames flowing beneath it. Was this really the place for me?

I went in and was asked to take a seat by a very pleasant receptionist. I noted the orchids, fresh floral displays and leather furniture. I had only been sitting for a few minutes when I was approached by a friendly blonde lady with clear blue eyes. She said her name was Joanne and asked me to follow her up to her office. We went to the top floor using the lift and enjoyed a bit of friendly banter. I had tea and a tour and when I left Jo said she would be in touch with dates for a formal interview. I had obviously passed the first test.

When I got home, I decided to call Iris; it had been almost five years since I last saw her, but I just felt the need to go again. This was a huge step. I might not get the job of course, but if I did would it be wise of me to take it? I was happy at Pinehill, I knew everyone, it took very little effort to get there. On the other hand, this was an excellent opportunity, £20,000 more per year plus bonus, and a chance for me to really prove myself and become part of the world-class hospital group, Hospital Corporation of America, HCA who owned the Portland Hospital in London where Princesses Beatrice and Eugenie had famously been born. They also owned the Wellington, London Bridge and the Princess Grace to name but a few. I knew The Lister had one of the longest established and most successful fertility clinics in the country. I had read that one in three of their patients travelled from outside London because of the exceptional care and treatment they offered.

I saw Iris, again we just seemed to be having a natter in her front room. She vaguely remembered me and asked why I had come to see her. I simply said I had a decision to make. We chatted, and several people came through to me with messages, again, some made sense, some did not. Suddenly Iris said, 'This decision you need to make is about a job.' I nodded. 'You didn't go looking for the job, it came looking for you.' This was not a question. 'I feel that the job is yours for the taking. It will be a good move for you.' That was all I needed to hear.

My interview date came and went; I met Jemma in her workplace beforehand, she was working at One Great George Street at that time, and we enjoyed a tasty lunch while she helped to calm my nerves. As I left the hospital after my interview, I knew, without a shadow of a doubt, that I wanted to work there. I was interviewed by Gill, the Chief Nursing Officer, and Jo who was Clinical Services Manager. We chatted, and I instantly liked both women and felt I could work for them and with them.

Gill explained that they had more interviews to conduct and that I may not hear anything for about a week. We shook hands and off I went into the cold afternoon air to tell Mike all about it.

I felt exhausted when I got home, the adrenaline and the travelling had taken its toll. I wondered if Iris had been correct. She had also told me that I would live in the country one day and that looked far from being a possibility.

I had been home for about half an hour when the phone rang, it was the nursing agency. I was told that I had been offered the position. Would I accept? I immediately said yes and the whole process got underway very quickly. I was going to work in London.

After a two-week induction which took me to different venues around London, including HCA Headquarters in Marylebone Road, I was ready to start at The Lister and get to know my new department. As well as my daily commute, I had to get used to wearing my own clothes all day. I had always worn a uniform to work. This was a different ball game. At first, I enjoyed it and found myself planning what to wear the night before as well as choosing jewellery. When a nurse is in uniform there are strict health and safety and infection control protocols. No jewellery, except for a plain wedding band, no stones in rings allowed. No nail varnish and nails are kept short. Hair is either worn up or must be above the collar in length. I couldn't bring myself to wear nail varnish, but quickly got used to wearing rings, bracelets and necklaces. It was a good excuse to go clothes shopping, but I missed my uniform if truth be told.

A couple of weeks before I took up my position at The Lister I stabbed myself in the hand with a knife while trying to get the stone out of an avocado. Another trip to Accident and Emergency ensued (did I mention that I am a bit accident prone?) I started work sporting a spectacular bruise on my left hand. During my introduction to one of our most eminent consultants, he pointed out of the window to the car park and said, 'That is where the last outpatient manager is buried.'

I looked him directly in the eye and retorted, 'Do you see that bruise on my hand? That was the last Consultant who upset me.'

Thankfully he roared with laughter; I thought I was going to have to scrape Jo off the floor when I told her about it.

From the outside, The Lister is a classic example of London's Victorian gothic style, but inside it is bright and tastefully decorated. It has state-of-the-art medical equipment. I found the critical care unit to be an ultra-modern fascinating department. However, office space is scarce, and my first office did not have a window, but Suzy Jones, who was the Chief Operating Officer at that time, (she became Chief Executive Officer) arranged for me to move up to the third floor to share an office with Susannah, the Chief Nursing Officer's personal assistant. Susannah and I hit it off immediately and developed a great working rapport. We would be visited regularly by Jo and many of the other heads of department and enjoyed lots of friendly office banter.

The food was wonderful, there was always a wide variety to choose from. The patient *à la carte menus* were incredible, and the food was impeccably presented, just as you would expect from a hospital with a world-class reputation. Indeed, it is what was expected from the clientele which include royalty from around the globe, and the *crème de la crème* of society. Obviously, I am not at liberty to name names, but there were some very famous faces indeed.

Although I was based at The Lister, I was also responsible for overseeing the Chelsea Consulting Rooms, in Lower Sloane Street, and often went to the Chelsea Outpatient Department in King's Road to liaise with the Outpatient Manager there. Also, because private healthcare insurance was offered to full-time employees, I could get some invaluable physiotherapy for my back problems at

280 King's Road. I enjoyed walking to Lower Sloane Street to visit the private GP surgery. The walk took me past the Royal Hospital, home of the Chelsea Pensioners. It is a grade I and II listed building and was founded by Charles II. King Charles issued a royal warrant in 1681 to build a hospital to care for soldiers 'broken by age or war'. I loved seeing the men and women dressed in their scarlets and blues. They were mostly in their everyday blues and shako caps embroidered with the letters 'RH'. I found out that they could only wear these uniforms within a two-mile radius of the hospital. I adored seeing them wearing their iconic scarlet coats and tricorn hats on special occasions.

One such occasion was at Christmas time. Annually, The Lister management staff, consultants and their partners, are invited to a Christmas carol service in the Wren Chapel at the Royal Hospital. I was stunned by the beauty of the chapel. Built between 1681 and 1687, was designed by Sir Christopher Wren who had been given no restrictions or limitations regarding the design. A striking painting depicting the Resurrection, is in the half dome of the apse and was created by Sebastiano Ricci. It dates to 1714. The chapel was tranquil as well as magnificent, still possessing its original wainscoting and plaster work. The ceiling is forty-two feet high in places. I was in awe of the beautiful structure. The service was moving and inspiring. I watched in reverence as the scarlet-clad pensioners handed out the hymn sheets, mingling with the congregation who were sitting in the oak pews covered with rich velvet cushions. I could hear the tapping of their highly-polished boots as they trod gently across the pristine black and while floor. I relished listening to the choir perform in such a remarkable setting. Two Christmas trees flanked the altar, adding to the ambiance. At the end of the service, we walked across to the Great Hall past flaming torches for a wonderful Christmas soiree. The whole evening was magical, twinkling Christmas lights and trees, floral displays and candles adorned the room. The Sir Christopher Wren designed buildings were magnificent and I felt very honoured to have been invited.

I made a point of visiting as many other HCA Hospital Outpatient departments as I could, to learn how they operated and hopefully share information to make sure I was providing the best service I possibly could. I soon learned how to get to and from The Portland, The Wellington and London Bridge Hospital, and was amazed by how quickly I became a street wise Tube user, which included getting irritated by tourists, especially ones with giant backpacks, meandering along the platforms and failing to stand on the right of the escalators. My new go-to shop became Peter Jones in Sloane Square, it was by far the nearest and easiest shop for me to frequent when I needed to buy Christmas or birthday presents. I also discovered some great shoe shops in King's Road, which often had incredible sales.

The King's Road (it literally had been King Charles II Road, linking St James's Palace with Fulham) was where Starbucks opened its first coffee shop in Britain at number 123 in 1998. In the 1950s coffee shops and bars were becoming popular in Britain. Gina Lollobrigida opened the Moka espresso café in Frith Street around 1953. The Fantasie coffee bar at number 128, was the first in the King's Road, and opened in 1955. It was in the Fantasie that Mary Quant planned her now famous boutique, Bazaar, which became birth place to the 'Chelsea look', the 'mod' era and of the mini skirt (which had been requested by customers who wanted skirts to become shorter and shorter) and named after Mary's favourite brand of car.

The last thing I wanted to do at the weekend was go near shops, so it was easier to pick something up on the way home from work. I also opted for online grocery shopping too. Mike had retired by then and was looking after the house in the way that most men do, enough said about that, so I ended up employing a cleaner too. My life had completely changed, and I was not sure how comfortable I felt about it.

*

In September 2013, we went to a Heads of Department retreat at Coworth Park in Ascot which borders Windsor Great Park (the place Prince Harry spent his last night as a bachelor). The hotel is part of the Dorchester group and was an opulent venue. We worked hard during the day creating plans to lead our departments and ultimately the hospital into an exciting new phase, punctuated by sumptuous tea breaks and lunches. We were rewarded for our hard work with exquisite food, wine and entertainment in the evenings. My room was delightful, with a large copper bathtub and four-poster bed, and I really wished Mike could be there to share the experience. On the last day, we had the option to have some time to ourselves and to choose some activities to partake in. Spa treatments were popular with the ladies, but I decided to try Segway racing, shooting and sheepdog trials (we used very cute and very clever ducks instead of sheep). It was tremendous, and great fun. I also managed a swim in the spa pool which had underwater music and was bounded by amethyst plinths. All in all, it was a very worthwhile and enjoyable experience. I returned to work fired with enthusiasm and new ideas. We were already a world-class hospital serving royalty, the rich, famous and elite, but we were about to take it to another, sensational level and I was excited to be a part of it.

I was invited to attend a fund-raising event which was held in The Caledonian Club in Belgravia. Richard Smith was one of our consultants at The Lister, and he is the leader of the UK Uterine Transplantation research team. He has donated the royalties from his last two books to the charity. The Belgravia mansion which houses the club, founded in 1891, is stunningly beautiful and amazing art work hangs on the walls. It was such a privilege to attend that important event. I had often shared friendly banter with Richard, a fellow Scot. I used to tell him his accent made me feel homesick. He is an extremely friendly and down-to-earth man and a brilliant surgeon. A truly remarkable man.

It was decided that I should become the Safeguarding Lead for Paediatrics in the hospital, answering of course to the Chief Nursing Officer. I went to the Portland Hospital for two days and completed Level 4 (intercollegiate) Training for named nurses. As part of my ongoing training I also attended a course in Supervision Skills in Child Protection which was organised by the National Society for the Prevention of Cruelty to Children. This meant three days in Harley Street with a two-day follow-up session the following month. On the Thursday of the first week, I headed to The Lister to catch up with my team and attend the monthly HOD's meeting before heading up to Scotland. I had originally taken the day off but decided it would be prudent to go to work for a catch-up before my long Easter weekend break given that I had been in Harley Street all week.

After the meeting, I headed straight out the door and started to walk quickly towards Victoria Station. I was determined to get back in plenty of time for my hair appointment before driving north. In my haste, I tripped on a paving stone, and before I knew what had happened I was stretched out on Ebury Road feeling dazed. I had heard my nose crack as it hit the pavement, so was not surprised when the nice man who came to my aid, called an ambulance and stated to the operator that my nose was obviously broken. I remember sitting on a chair which had been hastily brought out of a nearby shop and calling Mike to say the trip to Scotland that afternoon was most definitely not happening. I then called Susannah and sobbed at her down the phone. By the time, she got to me I was in the back of the ambulance happily puffing on gas and air from a tube, not a mask, feeling very lightheaded and giggly. My wrist was hurting too, the left one that had all the metal work in it from the fall I had in America. Susannah reassured me that my nose didn't look too bad; I had visions of looking like a boxer and my nose being spread across my face, so declined her offer of a compact mirror.

I was taken to the local Accident and Emergency department, and it was confirmed that my nose and wrist were in fact broken. I felt very badly shaken up and longed to get home. Thankfully Mike came to meet me, I don't think I could have made it home by myself.

Prior to this accident, I had been thinking about my future. My latest appraisal had been a good one, and Jo told me I could look forward to moving to the next level of management within HCA. I had a coach, which was not uncommon for employees, and she had asked far-reaching questions about my ambitions, personal development and plans for the outpatient department. The questions really got me thinking. Was this what I really wanted to do? Once I had started on the course that was being planned for me, there would be no going back. I had always wanted to write and paint. I loved gardening and walking our dogs, Oscar and Stella. Mike was at home all the time; I barely saw him except for a couple of hours at night, and weekends when I was tired. We had only been married for a couple of years, was this the routine really what I wanted?

We did make it to Scotland eventually, and when we returned I was due to attend a seminar in the Dorchester which would run over two days. I think if I had been on my normal daily commute, which I could now do without thinking, even knowing exactly which train and Tube carriage to choose for optimum time saving, I would have been okay, but I found the journey to the Dorchester stressful. Ordinarily, it would not have bothered me, but my confidence had been shaken to the core. I was afraid to walk in the middle of the pavement, I had to hang on to railings when going up and down stairs at Tube stations. I felt vulnerable. I walked into the hotel acutely aware of my heavily bruised face and black eyes. I felt embarrassed and almost as if I was letting the side down. I found it very hard to concentrate and eventually burst into tears. Jo was great as always. I had been experiencing several health issues of late and she was so understanding and supportive. In the end, I went home, I would love to say reluctantly, but it was with relief. I made an appointment with my GP and was signed off work for two weeks.

The fall had been a catalyst, and I knew it. It was decision time again. I was in the fortunate position to be able to take early retirement when I reached my 55th birthday which was not too far away. Did I want the high-powered job in Chelsea with all the benefits that came with it, or did I want a much quieter existence with time to pursue my dream of researching my family tree, writing a book and painting. Mike and I discussed it at length. I would be losing my salary, but, I would no longer need to fork out a huge amount of money on rail and tube travel. I could clean the house myself again, and shop around for bargains. I certainly wouldn't miss catching the 06:57 to King's Cross every morning and returning home no earlier than 19:00, often later if I had meetings to attend, even if they were held in a restaurant on the King's Road or in the Sloane Club, a meeting is a meeting, and the journey home at the end of the evening was a long one. We have one life to live. I had an amazing job which offered wonderful opportunities, but was that what I wanted to do with the bulk of my time? I had never been ambitious or sought promotion, it had just sort of happened, I often asked myself how I got here. This sounds ungrateful, and I truly do not mean to sound flippant, I had worked very hard, and it had paid off. There was now a distinct fork in the road and I wasn't sure which direction to choose.

CHAPTER 27

RETIREMENT

"There's never enough time to do all the nothing you want."
- Bill Watterson, *Calvin and Hobbes*

"Auld Ayr, wham ne'er a town surpasses, For honest men and bonny lasses."
- Robert Burns, *Tam O'Shanter*

As I have already mentioned, my accident had been the catalyst which would bring about a change in career direction. If I hadn't fallen over that day, would I still be working at The Lister? Who knows? After careful consideration and many discussions with Mike, I decided to hand in my notice. I had thoroughly enjoyed working for HCA at The Lister, I had been to many places which I probably wouldn't have visited. I had experienced the daily commute, and the buzz of working in London. I had met many fascinating people and made some lovely new friends. The Lister would be the last entry on my CV and I was tremendously proud of that fact. When I started my nurse training back in 1978, I never imagined that I would end up working in a world-class hospital in London, in charge of the outpatient and laser departments, and a suite of GP consulting rooms in lower Sloane Street. When I was, young and met my friends in King Street in Kilmarnock to shop for clothes in Chelsea Girl and tried out make up in Boots, I could not have imagined I would be shopping regularly on the King's Road in Chelsea. If I had imagined it, I could not have anticipated how I would get there.

I have the odd day here and there when I have regretted my decision, but too few to mention. I did some bank work back at Pinehill for a short while, but my heart just wasn't in nursing any more, and I decided to let my registration lapse at the end of last year. It was thought provoking to receive the letter of confirmation from the Nursing and Midwifery Council. It was official. I was no longer entitled to practice as a nurse, but any feelings of doubt passed too quickly for me to consider that I may have made the wrong decision.

I signed up for a Creative Writing course in Letchworth run by an amazing lady called Elizabeth Barber. One of my comrades in the group, Paul Walker, has just published his first (of many I am sure) and in my opinion, excellent, novel. I also auditioned for an award-winning society called Hitchin Thespians. It was founded in 1902 and is one of the largest and oldest amateur operatic societies in the country. Lesley was already a member and she had told me all about it. Lisa helped me to prepare for my audition after suggesting that I should sing, 'Wishing You Were Somehow Here Again' from Andrew Lloyd Webber's Phantom of the Opera, which I did. I was accepted and thoroughly relished taking part in the annual Hitchin Thespians 'Christmas at Woodside' concert. Jemma, Andy, Lisa and Alex came along to enjoy the music, mince pies and mulled wine and to cheer me on. It was wonderful.

Mike and I were kept busy gardening, building a patio (that is another rather long story for another time) and walking our two dogs, Oscar the gentle German Shepherd, and Stella our rescue Staffy-cross dogs. That said, Oscar did disgrace us once in Blakeney, Norfolk. We were staying in a lovely dog-friendly hotel, it was October, the weekend that the clocks were turned back by one hour. We left the dogs in our room while we went to the dining room for breakfast. Oscar could hear us returning and jumped up excitedly at the door and managed to lock it. It was cold, so we hadn't left any windows open. To cut a long story short, the handyman was called out to break down the door, bringing an end to an extra hour in bed for the rest of the guests.

I found I had time to paint and of course as I mentioned, researching my family tree was all consuming at times. We had lovely holidays and life was good.

Figure 50: *Lisa, Albert Hall rehearsal*

Lisa Joined the London Philharmonic Choir and, much to my delight, regularly performed in the Classical Spectacular concerts which were held in the Royal Albert Hall. I had been to see Classical Spectacular many times, with its state-of-the-art technology, laser displays and thundering cannons which boomed in time to Tchaikovsky's 1812 Overture finale, but it was truly mind-blowing the first time I went to see Lisa perform in it.

Mum and Dad managed to attend one of Lisa's Christmas concerts in the RAH which was extremely special, since it was also their first visit to the venue.

Lisa and Alex moved to Ely in Cambridgeshire, which is a beautiful cathedral city. The cathedral itself is stunning, it was built between 1083 and 1375 but has origins going back to AD672. I like to visit when the cathedral plays host to the annual Christmas fair. Lisa and I happily wander around the magnificent craft and food stalls nestled within the cathedral walls taking in all the sights, sounds and tastes of the festive season.

Jemma and Andy lived in South London when I first retired, and so I got to see them on a regular basis too, and spend time with Maxy (more commonly known as Maxy Moo, or Granma's wee man!) their bichon/poodle cross dog whom I adore. But as ever, circumstances were about to change again. Jemma and Andy announced that they were moving to New York. They were delighted, as was I, but I knew it was the end of an era and that I would miss them terribly. All six of us had spent most Christmases and Easter weekends together, had countless summer barbecues, it had been wonderful and we had lots of great memories, not to mention photographs, but now that era was coming to an end and another exciting chapter was hopefully opening for all of us.

Mike's dad Monty became unwell and was sadly diagnosed with cancer. He died after what was, thankfully for him, a short time. Mike and I decided that it was time for us to sell the bungalow and relocate to Scotland. Mike was heartbroken about his dad's passing, but knew it was time to move on. We knew that my mum's health was deteriorating, and would continue to do so, and that Dad, understandably, was finding it difficult to cope as her illness progressed. We wanted to move to Scotland to be near at hand and to help out.

The bungalow sold very quickly, and before we could draw breath we had bought a 200-year-old farmhouse in the Ayrshire countryside... so Iris had been correct in her prediction after all.

Jemma and Andy moved to New York, settled in quickly and I soon paid them a visit, enjoying the ambience and unique atmosphere that only New York can offer. Jemma is a dog walker by day and stage manages shows on a regular basis by night. She has recently begun to take part in a performance here and there which is fantastic. She is incredibly happy which of course makes me happy.

Lisa joined the BBC Chorus which meant she would be performing in the Last Night of the Proms.

Now, just so that you fully understand, I have longed to attend the Last Night of the Proms for as long as I can remember. I have relished watching the flag-waving throngs of people in the Royal Albert Hall singing along to Edward Elgar's Land of Hope and Glory and Hubert Parry's Jerusalem and this year, 2018, in the exalted company of Sir Andrew Davis, Gerald Finlay, Jess Gillam and Lisa Bartley, my dream finally came true.

Figure 51: *Oscar and Stella*

Mum was admitted to an excellent nursing home which specialises in dementia care. Caring for her 24/7 became too much for Dad, who as an octogenarian, has his fair share of health issues. He wanted her to remain at home, but in the end, he had to (reluctantly) agree with the health professionals that Mum required professional care and contacted Dundonald House. My sister-in law Dee is practice manager in the Dundonald doctor's surgery, and she had been impressed by what she had seen and heard. Since being admitted Mum has taken part in French classes and is about to start learning some Italian! Every Friday afternoon there is a sing a long, usually featuring old Scottish songs which are familiar to all the residents. The staff are simply amazing, and I can't praise them enough, and as for the chef's apple pie, well, it is absolutely delicious. Alzheimer's is an inexorable, ruthless and merciless condition. It is heartbreaking to watch Mum deteriorate and the effect it has on Dad. Dad visits every day and the tenderness I have witnessed between my parents has brought tears to my eyes on many occasions. I know without any shadow of a doubt that they truly love each other dearly.

*

Mike and I love living in Scotland. I can see much more of my two brothers, Jim and Alastair, and my two lovely sisters-in-law, Karen and Dee, not to mention our adorable niece and nephew Holly and Billy. We have reconnected with old friends, Jean and Philip Murphy have been fabulous, and made new friends.

Figure 52: *Holly and Billy*

My wee (six-foot-five) cousin came over from Canada to stay with us for a month. He really enjoyed being back on his home turf, catching up with all the family (and he makes a mean curry completely from scratch). We adore living close to the sea and walk on the beach twice every day. Well, Mike does, sometimes I am too busy writing and painting (that is my excuse and I'm sticking to it). We have wonderful neighbours, but most importantly we have each other, and it doesn't get much better than that.

"Change is inevitable; but progress depends on what we do with that change."

- Charles Wheelan

I suppose I should really have called this memoir King Street, to the King's Road and Then Back Again, but it is a bit too wordy. I will end with one of Gran's favourite sayings:

'What's for ye, will not go by ye.'

Figure 53: *Jacqueline, Oscar and Stella.*
In memory of my beloved Oscar Dog who died 31st December 2018.
He sat beside me day after day whilst I wrote this book.

My boy Oscar

Soft brown eyes, ever watchful,
Huge paws to pounce and protect
Jowls which could maim, but offer kisses,
So gentle, but none would suspect.

You gave faithful, unconditional love
Companionship and joy
You will be in my heart forever
My beloved darling boy

How I got to King Robert the Bruce

Grandfather, James Heron

My grandfather James Heron was born on the 1st of May 1913 in Moscow, Ayrshire. He married my grandmother Margaret Sawyers-Hogg Durnie on December 27th 1935 in Kilwinning, Ayrshire. My dad was born in 1938.

Great-Grandfather, James Heron

My great-grandfather, also James Heron, was born in Nethercribben, Holywood, Dumfriesshires in 1882. He married my great-grandmother, Maggie Barnes on the 16th of June 1911. I managed to get a copy of the marriage certificate and found out that Great-Granta married at the age of 25, he was ploughman and his usual residence was Hurleford. Great-Grannie was a country servant and her usual residence was Monkton.

Great-Grannie's mother was Jane Stevenson before she married, her father was James Barnes. The certificate also states that my great-grandfather's father was also James and that he was a ploughman. His mother Agnes's maiden name had also been Heron.

Great-Granta's death certificate reads that his father was Thomas Heron, a dairyman, not James. His mother is still recorded as Agnes Heron, maiden name also Heron. After a long time searching, I have found records for Thomas and none that match with the name James so that is what I have gone with. I know it is the correct death certificate, because my papa is recorded as his son, address, 35 Woodbank Road, Crosshouse. Cause of death is difficult to decipher, but looks like frontal haemorrhage, exacerbation, bronchitis recurrence and disability.

Second Great-Grandfather, Thomas Heron

According to the 1901 Scotland Census, Thomas was born 1861.

263

He was the head of the household and married to Agnes. He was born in Inch, Wigtownshire, the registration district was Kirkmaiden. His address was Killumpha Cottage and he was a ploughman. The list of household members is as follows:

Thomas Heron age 40

Agnes Heron age 42

James Heron age 19 (Granta)

Martha Heron age 14

Thomas Heron age 8

John Heron age 6

I found his birth certificate; he was born on May the 2nd 1861. His father was Thomas Heron, he was an agricultural labourer. His mother was Martha Heron, maiden surname Baird.

I also found Thomas's death certificate, it clearly states that he had been married to Agnes Heron and that his mother was Martha Heron, maiden surname Baird. His father is registered as Thomas Heron, dairyman. He died of peritonitis in Kirkmaiden Wigtownshire age 45 in 1906.

Third Great-Grandmother, Martha Baird

Martha Baird was born in Little Balyet, Inch, Wigtownshire in 1831. She married Thomas on the 26th of September 1848, she died in 1907.

Fourth Great-Grandfather, Major Baird

Major Baird was born in Wigtownshire in 1794. His father Samuel was 20, and his mother Janet was 18. I am not certain what happened to Janet, but he married again, this time to Grace Burgess on 29th of May 1821. He died in Inch, Wigtownshire in 1878.

According to the 1871 Scotland Census, he was 76, head of the household, and his address was Cottage Machar. His occupation is listed as agricultural labourer/pauper. Household members are listed as:

Major Baird age 76

Ann Baird age 35

James Baird age 12

Grace Baird age 10

William Baird age 8

Thomas Baird age 5

Fifth Great-Grandfather, Samuel Baird

Samuel Baird was born in Wigton, Wigtownshire in 1841. He married Jessie Bannatyne on the 15th of June 1858. Samuel was a farm servant in Ardrossan. Jessie had lived in Birchburn, Shiskine. Her father was Archibald Bannatyne, a house thatcher, and her mother was Janet McKinnon. His father was Major Baird and his mother was Grace Burgess.

Sixth Great-Grandfather, James Baird.

James was born in Wigtownshire in 1750. He died in Harding Kentucky, USA, in 1804.

Seventh Great-Grandfather, Thomas Baird

Thomas was born in Ireland, on the 1st of January 1724. He died in Falling Spring, Franklin, Pennsylvania, USA.

Eighth Great-Grandfather, John "Immigrant" Baird

John was born in Strabane, Tyrone, Ireland in 1671. His mother was Janet Bannatyne. He married Rebecca Skerrett in 1693, they had eight children. He died in Londonderry, Chester, Pennsylvania, US, in 1744 (see alternate branch at the end of this section).

Ninth Great-Grandmother, Janet Bannatyne

Janet was born on the 10th of June 1641, in Liberton, Midlothian. Janet married John Baird in 1664 in Midlothian, then married James Baird Beard. She died in 1676 in England.

Tenth Great-Grandfather, William Bannatyne

William lived in Midlothian, he was born in 1620. His father, John, was 20 when he was born. His mother Grizel was 17 years old. He then married Margaret Thompson on the 20th of July 1633 in Liberton, Midlothian. He died in 1690.

Eleventh Great-Grandfather, John Bannatyne

John was born in Lanarkshire in 1600. His father, William, was 35, his mother Maria was 46. He married Grizel Lockhart on the second of July 1621 in Clackmannan, Clackmannanshire. He died in Stirling in 1621.

Twelfth Great-Grandfather, William Sir Bannatyne

William's father was 45 when he was born in 1554. His mother, Katherine was 42. He married Marioun McClair in Orkney. Marioun died on the 30th of November 1622 in Lesmahago, Stirlingshire.

It is recorded that William Bannatyne, Orkney, Scotland,

Book, Marriages.

Collection, The Orkney-Testaments Inventories, 1573-1615

"at Burwick in South Ronnoldsay, on January 29th, 1614 debts owing by dead to: erle of Orknay-landmaillis, 11 meillis beir, £3, £33 & 3meillis flesch, 13s 4d, £2 William Bannatyne, teind, 2 meillis beir, £3, £6. Sum £41"

TEIND , tenth part FLESCH, flesh MEILLIS, ??

BEIR , e.g. to bear false witness

Thirteenth Great-Grandfather, George, Earl of Dalhousie Ramsay

In 1521, when George was born in Fife, his father Nicholas, was 33, his mother Isobel was 16. He married Elizabeth Lady Whitsome Hepburn in Midlothian, He died on 11th of February 1580, at Cockpen, Midlothian.

Fourteenth Great-Grandfather, Nicholas Sir Dalhousie Ramsay

Nicholas was born in Cockpen, Midlothian, in 1488. His father was 23, his mother Elene was 24. He married Isabel, Lady Kincardineshire in 1520. He died in May 1555.

Fifteenth Great-Grandfather, Sir Alexander III Lord of Dalhousie.

Alexander was born in 1465, in Cockpen Midlothian. He married Elene, Lady Horne and they had one son together. He then married Nichola Ker in 1508. He died at Flodden Field on the 9th of September 1513.

Sixteenth Great-Grandmother, Lady Elizabeth Douglas Angus

Elizabeth was born in 1398 in Aberdeenshire. Her father was 22, her mother, Mary, was 18. Elizabeth married three times and died in Gifford, East Lothian in 1448.

Seventeenth Great-Grandmother, Mary Princess Scotland

Mary was born on January 1st 1380 in Rothsay Castle, Bute. Her father Robert was 42, her mother Annabella, was 30. Mary married five times and died on March 20th, 1457 at Duntreath Castle, Strathblane, Stirlingshire.

Eighteenth Great-Grandfather. Robert Stewart King of Scots III

Robert was born in Dundonald Castle, Ayrshire, in 1337. His father Robert was 21. His mother, Elizabeth of Rowallan, Queen of Scotland, Countess De Strathearn Mure, was 17. He married three times. Firstly, to Mary Margaret, Countess of Menteith Graham. Then, Annabelle, "Queen Consort of Scotland" Drummond, and finally, Lady Muriella Keith Duchess of Albany. His son, James I "The Black Knight" Stewart, King of Scotland, was born in 1394. Robert died on April 4th, 1406, in Carrick, Fife. He was buried in Paisley.

Nineteenth Great-Grandfather, Robert Stewart II, the Steward

Robert was born by caesarean section in 1316 after his mother died in childbirth following a riding accident. His father was Walter (6th High Steward of Scotland) Stewart. Robert married Elizabeth of

Rowallan, and their daughter Elizabeth was born in 1346 in Dundonald. Robert died in 1390.

Walter was born in 1292 in Dundonald. He married Marjorie Bruce, daughter of Robert, Princess of Scotland. Walter died in 1326 in Bathgate Castle, West Lothian.

Twentieth Great-Grandmother, Marjorie Bruce, Princess of Scotland

Marjorie was born in Dundonald Castle in 1296. She married Walter 6th High Steward and died at Paisley Castle in 1316 in childbirth.

Marjorie Bruce, Princess of Scotland

Marjorie was the founder of the Stewart Dynasty. She was the only child born to Robert I, the Bruce. There seems to be some confusion with the actual date; on my family tree it is recorded as 1300, in other documents it is recorded as December 1296, coincidentally, the same month that Edward I of England, also known as 'Hammer of the Scots' invaded the town of Berwick which at that time was part of Scotland.

Her mother was Isabella, from the Clan Mar. She died soon after giving birth. Her father at that time was the Earl of Carrick, and Marjorie was named after her paternal grandmother, Marjorie, Countess of Carrick.

Marjorie's father did not marry again until she was about six years old when Elizabeth De Burgh became her stepmother. Her father was crowned King of Scots on the 27th of March 1306 at Scone in Perthshire and Marjorie became Princess of Scotland.

Her father was defeated at the Battle of Methven in June 1306. He decided to send his wife, sisters and Marjorie further north with the Countess of Buchan, Isabella MacDuff, but they were captured by the Earl of Ross who handed them over to the English.

Edward I of England sent his captors to various places as a sign of his strength and to punish Robert. Marjorie was sent to Watton Convent where Marjorie was in solitary confinement for the next four years. A cage had been built for her, the plan was to keep her on public view at the Tower of London, but Edward had a change of heart, not so for her aunts who had been imprisoned in wooden cages and kept in public view at Roxburgh Castle and Berwick Castle.

Edward died on the 7th of July 1307 and his son Edward II succeeded the throne. Marjorie was held captive for seven more years before being released around 1314, perhaps in exchange for English prisoners captured after the Battle of Bannockburn.

Walter, 6th High Steward of Scotland, had excelled in the battle and was rewarded with the hand in marriage to Marjorie. Her dowry included the castle and Barony of Bathgate in Midlothian. Two years later, a heavily pregnant Marjorie was riding in Gallowhill in Paisley. Her horse threw her fiercely to the ground and Marjorie went into immediate labour. Her baby, Robert, was born by caesarean section (the first accurate record of the operation since the birth of Julius Caesar), and Marjorie died a few hours later. A cairn now marks the spot where the tragic accident allegedly happened, causing the death of the beautiful Marjorie on the 2nd of March 1316.

It has been reported that her last words were, 'He's a laddie; I ken he's a laddie, he will be King.' This may or may not be a true account of what happened that day, but her foretelling did come true. Her son succeeded his childless uncle David II of Scotland in 1371.

Twenty-first Great-Grandfather, Robert Bruce I, the Bruce, King of Scotland

Robert was born in Turnberry Castle, Girvan in 1274. He died at Cardross Castle Dunbartonshire, the cause is thought to be leprosy. His mother, Margaret Carrick, died on the 27th of October 1292.

Robert was born on the 11th of July in 1274. He was distantly related to the Scottish royal family through his father. He was born in Ayrshire, and could speak Gaelic, Scottish and Anglo-Norman.

Robert supported William Wallace, and after Wallace's death, he became Guardian of Scotland. He was determined to win Scotland's independence from the English.

Defeated in his first two battles against the English, famously, Robert was inspired and encouraged to continue his fight for independence by watching a spider trying to climb the wall of a cave, swinging back and forth to anchor its web. The spider failed time after time, but on the thirteenth attempt it triumphed.

In 1314, at the Battle of Bannockburn, Robert defeated the English army which led to the establishment of an independent Scotland.

Robert the Bruce died in 1329 and was buried in Dunfermline Abbey. He had requested that his heart should be taken to the Holy Land. It was literally carried into battle, but only got as far as Spain before being returned to Scotland and buried in Melrose Abbey, hence the name Braveheart which should be attributed to Robert the Bruce and not to William Wallace.

Alternative Branch of Tree

From John "the immigrant" Baird, there is another branch of the tree. His mother was Janet Bannatyne.

Ninth Great-Grandmother

Janet Bannatyne who was born on the 10th of June 1641, Liberton, Midlothian. She died in 1676 in Aberdeenshire.

Tenth Great-Grandmother

Margaret Thompson, 1621-1642.

Eleventh Great-Grandfather

William Thompson; he was born on the 12th of August 1600, in Leith, and died on the 25th of April 1633, also in Leith.

Twelfth Great-Grandfather

William Thompson, 1570-20th February 1630. Died in Lanarkshire.

Thirteenth Great-Grandfather

Thomas Thompson, 1545-8th of February 1587, married Margaret S Henderson.

Fourteenth Great-Grandmother

Marion Cochran, 1520-1595, Lanarkshire, married James Thompson, 1524-1611.

Fifteenth Great-Grandmother

Lady Marion Elizabeth Lennox, Countess Argyll Stuart, was born on the 9th of April 1476 in Darnley Castle. She married Robert "That Ilk" Cochran. She died on the 9th of December 1529.

Sixteenth Great-Grandmother

Lady Margaret Christina Countess of Lennox Montgomery, born in January 1436 in Eglinton Castle, Kilwinning, and died on the 20th of July 1493 in Darnley Castle Renfrewshire.

Sir Alexander, 1st Lord Earl Montgomery, born in 1403, Ardrossan, Ayrshire, died in 1470, Eglinton Castle, Kilwinning, Ayrshire.

Eighteenth Great-Grandmother.

Lady Agnes Isles MacDonald Baroness Montgomery, born 1365, Isle of Islay. She married John Sempill, and then John Montgomery. She died on the 9th of March 1413, in Ardrossan.

Nineteenth Great-Grandmother

Lady Margaret, Princess of Scotland Stewart, born in Dundonald 1356, died in Argyll, 1410.

Twentieth Great-Grandfather

Robert II King of Scotland Stewart, born on the 2nd of March

1316. He died on the 19th of April 1390 in Dundonald Castle.

Twenty-first Great-Grandmother

HRH Lady Marjorie Bruce, 1296-1316.

Twenty-second Great-Grandfather

Robert "the Bruce", 1ˢᵗ King of Scotland, 7ᵗʰ Lord of Annandale, Earl of Carrick DeBruce 1274-1329.

Twenty-third Great-Grandfather

Sir Robert VI, Lord of Annandale "The Competitor" DeBruce, 1243-1304.

Books

Beattie, Frank, *Post-War Kilmarnock,* The History Press Ltd, 2008

Belden, L, Burr and De Decker, Mary, *Death Valley to Yosemite, Frontier Mining Camps Ghost Towns,* Spotted Dog Press, 2000.

Ferrier, Walter, M, *The North Berwick Story,* Royal Burgh of North Berwick Community Council, 1991

Forbes, David & Murray, Keir, *Dundonald Castle* Official Souvenir Guide.

Gardiner, Juliet, *The 1940's House,* 2000

Hughes, Katherine, *Short Life and Times of Mrs. Beeton,* Harper Perennial, 2006

Jamieson, Bruce, *North Berwick, Biarritz of the North,* East Lothian District Council, 1992

Johnson, LeRoy & Jean, *Julia, Death Valley's Youngest Victim. The Heroic Rescue of the Stranded 1849ers,* 1981

Malkin, John, *Pictorial History of Kilmarnock,* Alloway Publishing, 1989

McCrum, Mark & Sturgis, Matthew, *1900 House* Macmillan, 1999

McNulty, Elizabeth, *Chicago Then and Now,* Thunder Bay Press, 2000

Simon, Renee B, *Destination Long Beach, The Queen Mary Story,* The RMS Foundation Inc, 2001

Steele, James, *Queen Mary,* Phaidon Press LTD, 1995

Stewart, Gordon, *Old Auchans House, Dundonald, A Brief History,* 2015.

Waller, Maureen, *"A Family in Wartime" How the Second World War shaped the lives of a generation,* Conway, in Association with Imperial War Museums, 2012

Newspaper Articles

Baker, Rob, 'Mini Skirts, Soviet Spies and the Chelsea Palace-The fascinating History of The Kings Road', *The Telegraph*, 16th April 2018

Davies, Catriona, '20 Years on Britain still feels the effects of Chernobyl', *The Telegraph*, 01 April 2006

Osborne, Samuel, 'British Governments shambolic response to Chernobyl Disaster in newly released documents', *Independent*, Friday 29th December 2017

Websites

http://www.northberwick.org.uk

http://dundonaldcastle.org.uk/history

http://www.bbc.co.uk/history

http://standrewblackadder.org.uk

https://en.wikipedia.org/wiki/Donner_Party

https://en.wikipedia.org/wiki/Chernobyl_disaster

http://wombtransplantuk.org/uk-research-team

https://en.wikipedia.org/wiki/King%27s_Road

http://www.mcgonagall-online.org.uk/gems/the-tay-bridge-disaster

http://taybridgedisaster.co.uk/

https://www.johnniewalker.com/en-gb/whisky-guide/johnnie-walker-story/

http://www.futuremuseum.co.uk/collections/life-work/social-history/emergency-services/healthcare—

https://friendsofseafieldhouse.wordpress.com/history/

https://en.wikipedia.org/wiki/Seafield%2C_Ayr

https://en.wikipedia.org/wiki/Lister_Hospital,_Chelsea

http://www.thelisterhospital.com/about-us/history-of-the-lister-hospital/

https://en.wikipedia.org/wiki/BCG_vaccine

http://chcchealth.org/about/history/

https://en.wikipedia.org/wiki/Normal_Theater

https://en.wikipedia.org/wiki/Navy_Pier

https://www.tripsavvy.com/ducks-at-the-peabody-hotel-2321499

https://en.wikipedia.org/wiki/Death_Valley

https://en.wikipedia.org/wiki/Scotty%27s_Castle

https://www.history.com/topics/westward-expansion/donner-party

https://en.wikipedia.org/wiki/Donner_Party

https://en.wikipedia.org/wiki/Rhyolite,_Nevada

https://en.wikipedia.org/wiki/East_Fortune

http://www.witchcraftandwitches.com/trials_north_berwick.html

http://www.clan-duncan.co.uk/gellie-duncan-witch.html

https://www.historic-uk.com/HistoryUK/HistoryofScotland/Sawney-Bean-Scotlands-most-famous-cannibal/

https://en.wikipedia.org/wiki/Sawney_Bean

Television Programmes

Edwardian Farm. Acorn Media UK, A Lion Television

Production for BBC 2010, Featuring Peter Ginn, Ruth Goodman & Alex Langland.

Coming soon, a sneak peek, Dunoureald Castle

Catherine slipped on the slimy stone steps as she crept down towards the castle vaults. Catching her breath, she steadied herself against the cold, tallow-greased wall. Cautiously, she looked over her shoulder. Seeing and hearing nothing in the dimly lit cellar, she continued her descent down the stone spiral steps towards the secret tunnel which would take her out onto the shore and temporary freedom. She could hear sounds of tormented groaning and wailing coming from the nearby pit prison tucked away in the bowels of the castle. The horrific sound of human suffering, which made her feel physically sick, but Catherine, even at sixteen years of age, knew that there was more than one kind of suffering. Most people would consider her privileged, living a life where she was seemingly protected, and wanting for nothing, but suffer she did, albeit silently and compliantly.

She expertly felt her way along the walls of the dismal passageway, the only light being watery beams of moonlight struggling to squeeze through the arrow-loopholes set into the thick stone walls. She had come down these steps so often that she knew every crack, dip and where each non-uniform step height, deliberately constructed as a defence mechanism against would-be attackers, was located, and could navigate them easily in the darkness. She never brought a candle with her when she came down here; her young eyes quickly adjusted to the feathery slithers of moonlight, she preferred having both hands free to steady herself. Catherine had made this journey more often than she could remember, usually when there was a full moon, to escape the claustrophobic and oppressive atmosphere of the castle. A place where she was watched and controlled constantly. Her every move monitored by her step-father Earl De Durnie and his entourage of men and women eager to please the master. As she reached the heavy wooden door which was almost hidden from sight at the end of the passage, a faint sound startled her. Turning, she could see wisps of vapour as someone breathed in and out on the staircase which she had just descended. Catherine knew it was useless to try and hide; she stepped forward, commanding the person who was following her to show themselves. She had been certain that no one had noticed as she made her way down the narrow stairwell. Disappointment and dismay filled her being; she had only wanted a short walk, to be on her own, time to think, time to plan.

Suddenly she became aware of a wire-haired snout, nostrils flaring and emitting a fog of water vapour. 'Fergus,' she whispered. 'Come here, foolish dog.' On hearing his name, Catherine's faithful deerhound padded down the remaining stairs and stood by his mistress's side. His head almost level with hers, he nuzzled his cold wet nose into the folds of her heavy cloak, ecstatic to be reunited with his favourite person in the whole world, even although they had only been apart for less than an hour. Catherine wrapped her arms around his neck, stroking the grey-blue wiry mane. Fergus looked at her with his dark brown eyes and wagged his tail with utter delight and unconditional devotion.

Fergus was really her step-father's dog, used for deer coursing, but Fergus seemed to lack the instinct which had been expected of him, and he was frequently left behind when Earl De Durnie went hunting. The dog had been drawn to Catherine, perhaps sensing that she too failed to come up to her step-father's great expectations. Fergus could sense when Catherine needed him, for whatever reason, and he never failed to fulfil his duty towards her. They were almost inseparable, so Catherine was not altogether surprised to see him standing there looking up at her with love and adoration emanating from his kind and gentle face, an expression which was reciprocated wholly by Catherine herself. Suddenly, Fergus let out a slow, deep, barely perceptible growl and stared at the door partially hidden at the end of the passageway. Startled, Catherine quickly made her way to a dark, dank alcove which was situated to the left of the door. Green sea slime covered the five-foot-thick walls, and the air was sharp with the tang of salt. The castle had a moat, but this door led out to a secret tunnel which Catherine had stumbled upon during a game of hide and seek with Fergus. The tunnel stretched out under the moat and onto the rugged sea shore. Catherine had instinctively known not to mention her discovery to anyone; she thought of it as her secret place when she had found it a year ago. A place so different from the great hall and the upper floors which housed her family, soldiers and servants. Except, she now knew that the tunnel was used on a regular basis, but not by whom. Catherine crouched down into the dark shadows of the passageway and urged Fergus to remain quiet by wrapping her heavy wool cloak around his tall, narrow shoulders and stroking his head. The solid wooden door creaked and groaned almost painfully as it was forced open. Catherine could hear voices, men's voices, but did not recognise them. The figures were mere smudges against the glistening damp walls as a beam of moonlight shone in like a beacon of hope from the world outside.

Five men entered the castle. Catherine silently counted as each man passed the alcove unaware that they were being watched. Quietly and stealthily they made their way up the spiral staircase. Catherine listened as the great oak door at the top of the steps creaked open and the men entered the vast storage cellars which were situated beneath the main entrance hall and inner courtyard of the east wing. Instinctively Catherine knew something was very wrong. Why had the door to the secret tunnel been unlocked? Fergus growled quietly as if in agreement. She decided to leave the castle as she had planned, but instead of walking along the shore breathing in the cool night air and listening to the waves crash onto the rocky shoreline, she would hide and remain hidden until she knew that it was safe to return.

These were uncertain times. Just last year, the Scottish Act of 1563 had been established, making witchcraft a crime punishable by death. The act had stirred up feelings of suspicion and unrest amongst the people of Dunoureald. Many of whom pointed a finger at Jessie, a maidservant to whom Catherine was extremely close; a gentle, kind woman who was a natural healer using plants and herbs to cure minor ailments and diseases. Jessie in turn was very fond of Catherine, she staunchly looked out for her. It was Jessie who had comforted and cared for Catherine when her mother had been killed in a riding accident four years ago.

When Catherine was certain there was no one else in the tunnel waiting to enter, she arose from her hiding place, opened the door with difficulty, and stepped down onto the rocks below. Walking with one hand on the wall and the other clutching Fergus's mane, she could see moonlight shining in the distance and hear waves crashing onto the shore. The weather had suddenly taken a turn for the worse. The sound of the stormy sea echoed and bounced off the tunnel walls menacingly. As she left the shelter of the tunnel behind, Catherine thought quickly about where she could find shelter from the inclement weather and any possible hostility.

She headed for the doocot, the beehive-shaped structure situated next to the castle. She had often played hide and seek there with her brother when their mother had been alive, when they were allowed to play and were treated like human beings. Inside, the smell of bird dung took Catherine's breath away, she had forgotten just how strong and overpowering it was. Two hundred or so pigeon holes coiled above her towards the small circular opening in the domed roof. The birds provided much-needed eggs and meat for the castle, but right now, their home would provide much-needed shelter for Catherine and Fergus.

Feeling safe and warm from the elements, Catherine thought she may have been rather hasty in her judgement of the men who entered the castle, after all, she was not familiar with all the people who lived there or who came to visit. Preparations were well underway for a banquet being held in honour of her stepfather's forthcoming nuptials; maybe they were guests or musicians? There was sure to be a reasonable explanation. Maybe the men were returning from a hunting expedition? Maybe they had been seeking out smugglers who regularly frequented these shores? Maybe they were servants who had been gathering seaweed to dry and use as fuel? Suddenly, Catherine was brought back to the here and now with the sound of screaming, shouting and cannon fire.

ABOUT THE AUTHOR

Born in Ayrshire, Scotland, in 1959, Jacqueline began her general nurse training in 1978 and her midwifery training in 1981. Work and marriage took her from the small west coast Ayrshire village of Crosshouse, to Thurso in Caithness, North Berwick in East Lothian, Illinois, USA, the Cotswolds and Hertfordshire. Jacqueline returned to Ayrshire in 2017, with her retired policeman husband Mike and their two dogs Oscar and Stella. Now that she has retired from nursing, she is following her dream to write and paint. Jacqueline loves walking the dogs, gardening and spending time with her daughters; Jemma, who lives in New York with her husband Andy and dog Maxy-Moo, and Lisa, who lives in Ely, Cambridgeshire with her husband Alex and kitten Maisie May!

36985229R00163

Printed in Poland
by Amazon Fulfillment
Poland Sp. z o.o., Wrocław